# Departures
# from
# The Story Sessions

Edited by
Cherry Potts

ARACHNE PRESS

First published in UK 2019 by Arachne Press Limited
100 Grierson Road, London SE23 1NX
www.arachnepress.com
© Arachne Press 2019
ISBN:
Print: 978-1-909208-74-2
ePub: 978-1-909208-75-9
Mobi: 978-1-909208-76-6

Thanks to Muireann Grealy for her proofing.

Printed on woodfree paper in the UK by TJ International, Padstow.

*Intimate, salon-like. As if I'd stumbled into an invitation only séance peopled by the spirits of Victorian hucksters and exotic beasts.*

(Audience feedback The Story Sessions)

# Contents

**Introduction**
Cherry Potts

*The Story Sessions:*
*The live literature event that thinks it's a folk club*

The Sessions started in much the same way as Arachne Press, in a fit of irritation. On this occasion the annoyance was at the difficulty of finding a literature event in South London to showcase our writers.

Following our mantra of *if no one is doing what you are looking for, do it yourself,* I decided to trial a series of monthly themed events, and go for what I really wanted for a night like this. Taking a lead from folk clubs, we had headliners, support acts and floor spots – and Flash from the Floor was born. That was a lot of fun – the audience wrote 100 word flash fiction or poetry on the theme of the evening in the interval, and read them out before we got on with the main event.

Another initiative was the 'test bed' session where any writer could book the slot immediately before the interval and read a work in progress, and be given feedback written by the audience in the interval – never has an interval been so industrious!

Finding 'acts' was never a problem, and the themes came thick and fast, sometimes honed to showcase our headliner, sometimes tied to a significant date, some funny, some serious, but the quality was always impressive. We even got funding for one year to cover the readers' expenses and to have an artist in residence, the wonderful Annalie Wilson, who gave us an on-theme song each time and read for writers too far away to contribute in person.

There have been some real highlights over the course of the

seventeen sessions: the moving stories at one of our earliest events: *Armistice Tales*, Barbara Renel and Carrie Cohen duetting parts of *Rio* for Helen Morris's *Simon Le Bon Will Save Us* (later published in *Five by Five*), the audience wearing multiple hats for Bartle Sawbridge's *A Date for Maureen*, a choral-speaking Flash from the Floor, Math Jones's electrifying rendition of *Four Failures,* which led to me offering him a publishing contract on the spot and subsequently to the publication of *The Knotsman.*

Thanks to The Ivy House, Café of Good Hope and Brockley Deli for having us, but we never found quite the right balance of access, transport links and most importantly, *quiet*, (oh the dog fight in the front bar...) so reluctantly, after four years, we stopped.

However, having encountered so many new writers, I thought we might be able to make a permanent record of all the talent we met during the life of the Sessions, and that, in keeping with the traditions of the Story Sessions, it should have a theme. I contacted everyone who had read for us and asked them to make suggestions. *Departures* grew out of that as something broad enough to cover as many of their ideas as possible.

Many of the writers included in this anthology we have, of course, already published. This is what I set up the Sessions *for*, that, and to find new writers to publish – which worked. Nancy Charley, Emily Bullock and Barbara Renel I first met at the Sessions, and likewise Oscar Windsor-Smith. Zoe Brigley and Becky Ros I first discovered when they were read by others at the Sessions, being too far from us to read themselves. Gloria Sanders was initially reading other people's work as part of one of our *Brockley Max* sessions, and then revealed she was a poet herself. I've known VG Lee for years, and persuaded her to read for us at our LGBT History Month event.

*The Story Sessions* was an invigorating, sweet experiment, and I'm proud to be able to produce a permanent record on paper – you can watch a lot of the videos at *arachnepress.com/the-story-sessions/* if that takes your fancy – or read on!

# Stories

## The Change
Helen Morris

I had read, of course, about the symptoms of 'the change.' That time in a woman's life when she moves from being able to produce children, to not. Not that I ever had produced children, but the monthly wax and wane of my cycle had been as much a rhythm to my life as my own heartbeat. The rhythm that had set the tides of my life for four decades.

I had read, of course, about the hot flushes, the mood changes, the loss of bone density. I had waited as my clock ticked downwards for the time I too would begin 'the change.' I thought I was ready. I thought I knew all there was to know. Ah my friends, I did not.

I found, when the time came, that my own personal 'symptoms' were not in the literature. They were not on Google. Nor in the 'older mums' posts on Mumsnet. They were not even whispered over large glinting glasses of Sauvignon blanc in velvet dark wine bars.

Hot flushes? Yes. I'd read about that. I was ready for that. I had read up diligently on the choices before me. I was prepared to stand in a suitably Shakespearean pose in some cluttered doctor's surgery and movingly enact: 'to HRT, or not to HRT – that is the question'. I was ready for that.

But I was certainly not ready for having a spanning pair of red and gold leathery wings erupt suddenly through my back. No. No, I had not been ready for that. I had not been ready, standing in the back garden that evening, holding my dusk pirate's rum and black. Watching the setting sun and feeling a cool spring breeze blow – and suddenly having the power of flight.

No.

I am not a panicker by nature. I have walked a path alone and relied upon my own self too long to panic. Panic is for those who are used to company. However, I am a swearer of some accomplishment. And I am pleased to say I did myself proud. Had anyone been watching I am not sure which they would have been more shocked to witness erupt from the middle-aged woman before them: glorious red and gold wings or the stream of luminous swear words. I may have even created a few new ones.

My mind and mouth were ablaze as I turned to study a rather spectacular profile in the French window glass. I am tall and strongly built. A product of a long line of blacksmiths, from times when trades were passed down from father to son and from mother to daughter. I have to say I looked magnificent. I turned from side to side to admire my resplendent reflection. The wings were heavy. I felt the muscles in my back tense and hold. When I spread the wings – my wings – wide, it hurt. I was going to need to start working out if they were staying. 'Bingo: wings', I mused. I stretched my left hand above my shoulder and felt my left wing, turning my head to look at the pliant surface. It felt warm and I could feel the touch of my fingers upon it. Like a bat's wing. 'Yo, bats,' I whispered, stroking my wing tip, 'no longer the only flighted mammal...'

And then as quickly as they had come I felt them retract and disappear. I caught my breath and the suddenness and the momentum pushed me forward onto the balls of my feet. These were not imaginary, they were large and physically real. I had felt them retract into me and I was physically as before, but yet not as before. I knew they hadn't entirely gone. They were waiting. Waiting for what?

'Bloody hell.' I thought seriously about what I should do in the circumstances. Then, decisively, I went in for another drink. I was shaking now, but exhilarated. I poured a suitably generous rum and swigged it. And as I did so I remembered Aunt Cherry. She would have appreciated the timing.

Aunt Cherry had always been the naughty aunt. Determinedly single, extravagantly bohemian and gloriously bisexual. She burned a bright path. A path that was then easy for me to follow. Her real name was Elsie. But she had taken to wearing cherry velvet as a girl and so, in the grand traditions of family nicknames, she had always been Aunt Cherry. I wrote to her at random intervals – holidays, birthdays and on the rare occasion I did something cultured. And I saw her at Christmas and once or twice in the summer when I visited my mother. She lived in the village next to the one in which I had grown up. A trio of sisters spread across Wootton, Cumnor, Appleton. I remembered her now because of that wedding.

It must have been a decade ago. My cousin's wedding. Not Cherry's child. She, like me, was childless. The fourteenth of February and a bride dressed in scarlet silk and oxblood red Doc Martens. Unseasonably warm. Me, waiting for the interminable photos to be over, and escape to be at hand.

I stood outside the Register office vaguely smiling at relatives in a way that I hoped was sufficiently off-putting to stop anyone coming up and making conversation. It had worked well enough. But it was not enough to stop Aunt Cherry. 'Hello dear,' she said crisply. 'Fucked anyone interesting recently?'

'Hello Cherry,' I said. 'Not since the Belgian mixed doubles badminton team last October sadly.' She smiled. She looked at me sideways.

'This will seem a strange thing for me to say, dear, but one day you'll understand why – when the change comes, you must come to me. You'll know when. I won't say any more now.' She turned and looked at me, and I, who can read people well, could not read her expression. She was like a jar that had lost its label and I could not see the contents inside through the opaque glass. 'Come to me. It's a family thing. I'll explain then.'

And she nodded once and strode away. She must have been seventy, but she walked tall and upright, not wearied by the boredom of a wedding, not bowed by gravity's pull. I assumed that she was going to pass down some old family herbal remedy to me. I hoped it involved alcohol. A menopause cocktail.

*The long slow hot flush* maybe? *The osteoporosis buster? The invisible woman?*

That's what I'd thought at the time. It wasn't what I thought now.

And so I found myself back in the next village to the one where I had grown up. Immediately I felt the teetering uncertainty of fifteen again. I paused with my hand on the rounded top of Cherry's green and silver lichened front gate. I hadn't rung to say I was coming. Aunt Cherry was eighty-two now. Where would she be?

The answer, it seemed, was waiting for me in the front garden. She smiled as I approached although it was not a smile of greeting or joy. It was a smile of recognition. The smile you give your siblings at a funeral.

'Hello,' she said. 'I've got a Lagavulin ready. What colour are your wings?'

And so we sat in her living room next to the wood-burner that pushed a dry heat rhythmically into the spring-chilled air. She told me the stories of a trade handed down from woman to woman for generations.

The Noctivagator.

I am a Noctivagator. I am a Fiur Fury. As is she, as was her aunt before her and so on and so on. Handed down through the female line for eons. Across nations. Across continents. The powers emergent at menopause and only in those without children. Legend says this is as a means of protection. What we fight has no mercy. It smells line descendants and slaughters them. Now I've fought them, I understand that.

So I sat with Cherry as her words became a tide that crept in and through me and changed my life. At my age you think you know yourself. You don't. I crossed her threshold one woman, and left another.

It takes a while to adjust. That's one bit of advice that is true. Control takes time. In the early days the crepuscular times are the most difficult. One Thursday my wings nearly launched in the snacks aisle in Aldi. I stood backed up against the twiglets clutching a family pack of Wotsits to my chest while I fought their urge to unfurl. Many a sweary half hour came and went in pub toilets attempting to re-fold them while they fought back like a poltergeist-possessed pop-up tent. Staggering around in a tiny cubicle alternately head butting the walls and muttering 'Get the fuck in'. No one stayed long in the next cubicle. 'The Change', I muttered to waiting friends when I emerged flushed. Entirely accurate – wholly misleading.

Slowly you adapt. You learn control. You discover your powers. You use them. Follow your dreams they say. Although I did once dream that I jumped out of a plane with just a pair of paper knickers as a parachute. So maybe not. But everyone dreams of being a superhero.

I've been a Noctivagator for five years now. Our powers are based on our individual human strengths. So we're essentially a powered up version of ourselves. Some women get huge physical strength, others phenomenal intelligence or speed. My friend Sheila, a fantastic cook, and an Erthe Fury Noctivagator can bake scones that turn into lava on impact. I always carry a few. If you don't need to use them in battle you can always eat one if you get a bit hungry. Her Noctivagant battle weapon is a cake tin. It's one of the ones with a detachable base. She calls it her loose bottom. I've seen her slice apart a momentous horde with it. It's also dishwasher safe so you don't have to scrub the sinewy bits off afterwards.

My power is based on my sharp tongue. Well it would be, wouldn't it. I have the power of *death by sarcasm*. An arch comment can stop a charging angel in their tracks and start them smouldering. Irony can fell them unconscious on the spot. Full sarcasm incinerates them on impact. I kill with words. Sarcasm is my weapon.

Angels? Yes. That's what we fight, us Noctivagators. In the best traditions of patriarchy, everything you think you know about good and evil is wrong.

I fight angels.

Please lay aside any of this *golden host* bollocks from your childhood. Please do believe in a set of enormously powerful extremely vicious supernatural beings who are looking for corporeal bodies to colonise. That means you. Nice, soft, warm human flesh. Consumed from the inside out. They don't colonise worlds. They colonise people. Like a big old parasite. Think of angels as being like huge voracious merciless tapeworms, but with a good publicist. I've been badly savaged by a cherub – before I managed to behead it with a sarcastic comment about dimpled buttocks. They have basalt teeth.

So, directly contradicting every school report ever, being mouthy has proved useful after all.

In battle it's me, my sarcastic gob and 'archangel slayer', my broadsword. Of course I have a broadsword. I'm not going out fighting the hordes of heaven with just a few scones and some harsh truths am I? This isn't Yorkshire. Sorry, let me just put your hair out. It's just a bit singed. Don't worry it'll be fine. Death by sarcasm isn't supposed to work on humans. You must have a slight seraphim infestation.

It'll be all cleared up now.

Anyway. Archangel slayer, my broadsword. I'm fifty-seven, I work for the council and in my spare time I save the earth with sarcasm, scones and a broadsword. I inherited her from Aunt Cherry. Cherry died three months ago in her sleep. Or that's how it looked. She was actually wasted by a Guardian Angel. They're the worst. Total bastards. Terrible spelling, too. Unforgiveable amongst the supernatural. If you can't leave a proper threatening message about unending suffering then where are you? Who's afraid of 'eternal surfing'?

So I inherited Cherry's broadsword. You inherit many things from your family. Some are useful. Some are a fucker frankly. Some feel like a burden when you first find them. But after a while, when they've been worn to your shape, they feel comfortable. Oh and did I mention the dragons? Aah the dragons.

The dragons fight with us.

I hunted the Guardian Angel that killed Cherry. It took me three weeks to find him. Let's just say he won't need help spelling 'eviscerated' again.

So here I am. Five years battle-hardened. You've caught me at a bit of a bad time to be honest. I'm just walking past the place where M&S used to be in the Harvey Centre. I parked in Terminus multi-storey, popped into Boots. And now I can feel the angels coming like the knife-point start of a migraine.

You can always feel angels coming. And they are coming now. We try to keep the battles away from the ground, from homes, from people. You don't want people getting in the way. The angels don't mind. I mind.

But there's no place for a supernatural battle quite like a car park. Highlander taught me that.

I feel the air tingling. I take three quickening steps and then break into a run – feeling myself powering up, growing stronger, growing taller. My wings erupt like a parachute and fan out and I beat them to angle me forward and power my run into a half flight. Jagged jade spines erupt outwards from each of my vertebrae. That's another leather coat ruined, but I look fucking awesome. Obsidian talons from my hands. I call it my Wolverine moment. The bones in my face push forward and my jaw makes room for my fangs. My beautiful sharp tongue studs and forks.

Two angels spiral towards me, their white rictus faces seething hatred.

I pull the air around me and punch up in a launch towards them. Skywards. Powerful. The drizzle sizzles around me.

'Hey boys,' I call. 'This is a scone in my pocket and I am pleased to see you.'

I am a Fiur Fury.

I am a Noctivagator.

Never, ever, ever underestimate a middle-aged woman.

I am changed.

## The Departure Board
David Steward


It's a game she plays from time to time, with rules of her own devising. The first step is to take a morning train from St Pancras to Paris. It requires a little forethought to book a cheap advance ticket, but once she's ready to move on, when she's earned enough from whichever mindless job she's been doing, an extra few days are bearable. From the Gare du Nord, she travels to another mainline station, buys a coffee, and looks at the departure board to choose a destination. Ideally, it should be at random, but she can never be sure how freely she makes her selection. There may be preferences or experiences lurking below the surface of her mind when she looks at the list of place names. Still, the novelty is enough. She'll be somewhere else by morning.

### Venice

In the crowd boarding the vaporetto at Ferrovia, she inadvertently knocks the rucksack from a man's shoulder. He shrugs away her embarrassment as she hands it back. When she mutters an apology in Italian, he answers in English. On the way to Ca' d'Oro, they exchange small talk. He's Nico, a commercial photographer, lives in London but was born in Shropshire. She's never been to Shropshire, she says. He's been working in Rome and is taking a few days off.

He suggests they have breakfast in a café which he knows, a couple of streets away from the flood of tourists in the Strada Nova. They stand among locals at a counter, with black coffee and pastries. When they meet for dinner that evening, he's polite and makes no demands. Diffidently, on their third night, he invites her to his room in a pensione on the eastern edge of

Dorsoduro, and they sleep together.

In the morning, as they wander through Burano towards the footbridge, she allows herself to wonder how it would be to live in a cottage here, and she chooses for her fantasy one painted azure blue, in a terrace between others in orange and pink. On spring mornings, she'd walk out early into the bustle around the boats on the narrow canal, shop for fresh fish and vegetables. Would she tire of it in time, she wonders, as it became familiar?

There's a fine mist floating on the lagoon and the moon is grey. The mist is called caigo in the local dialect, says Tim as he passes a can of fuel down from the jetty. Over supper last night, he talked about his art, about the life he's made here on Mazzorbo since he left England in the nineties, about meeting Nico for the first time at a photographic exhibition in the Guggenheim museum. Light-headed from the Soave, she fixed her gaze on the coloured bulbs over the terrace of the trattoria, trying to embed the evening in her memory. She felt animated, away from the routine of work, among creative people. This was the payback for months of drudgery. Nico and Tim were chatting with a fisherman who'd joined them at the table for a drink. Nico was at ease here. Watching him, she could tell he was adaptable enough to fit in anywhere, and she felt a growing affection.

It's Tim's idea that Nico and she should borrow his boat and see the dawn from Torcello.

The game has become theirs together now. Whenever Nico finishes an assignment, he calls her mobile and they arrange a day to meet in Paris.

### Barcelona
Except with girlfriends, she's never spoken about her parents before. She's confident enough now to open up, to make herself

vulnerable. She and Nico have ridden the funicular up Mount Tibidabo to the amusement park. On a terrace, looking down across the city to the sea, they drink cold beer.

She has no idea what kept her mother and father together, she tells him. Maybe there were moments of affection or happiness, but she can't bring any to mind. It's possible she remembers only the wrangling and the bitter silences because they were associated with a deep emotional reaction on her part. Looking back in her late teens, she came to suspect that her mother was oppressed by the limits of their life: the mid-estate house on the edge of a market town. Maybe she and her mother were more alike than she knew at the time, both with a preference for novelty.

Nico has a way of listening attentively, without interrupting, and she finds herself speaking freely, as if he's leaving her space to speak. She's experiencing, in a way that's new for her, the power of being listened to.

On the way down, she thinks wistfully of living in the heart of the Old Town, in a rented apartment, and knows she has these thoughts everywhere she goes. Always there's the same catch: you'd have to make a choice, to settle on one place for the long term. The advantage of her flat on the Caledonian Road is that it's a lock-up-and-go property. It will come to no harm, however long she's away.

### Berlin

On a warm Sunday morning, in a café near Europaplatz, Nico says he loves her.

'You too,' she says, without hesitating.

It's the first time in five years that she's said this to anyone.

### Toulouse

Over months, the rules of the game change. Now they take it in turns to choose a destination. Whoever makes the choice texts the other with a place name.

One weekend, they borrow a gîte in the Lot valley from a couple that Nico met when he did a food shoot in Paris. As they drive south in their hired car, the sun is dazzlingly low in a blue sky. Before Caussade, they turn off the *route nationale* and let the satnav guide them down minor roads through the shadows of woodland. The white house has an unfenced garden, shelving away to fields. After they've unpacked essentials, she pours glasses of pastis and they sit in deckchairs under a fig tree.

'In the summer,' he says, 'the fields down there are full of *tournesols*. They all face the same way, as if they're craning to watch you drive by. This is like no other countryside in my experience. You feel so close to the land. I could happily live here.'

It may be a throwaway remark, but it lands heavily with her. She's aware that a restlessness has been stirring recently, and any hint of settling down is bound to assume significance in her mind. Anything can become a routine in time. It disconcerts her when he pursues the subject. He's talking about buying a property.

'Can't you imagine yourself as a lotus eater in a place like this?'

She ignores the question and sips at her drink.

'The freedom's great,' he says, 'but you can't always be on the move, can you?'

She's surprised how emotional he becomes when she tells him how she feels. Through the night, he seems to swing from maudlin self-pity to anger and all the way back. Once, he accuses her of being afraid of commitment. She knows she isn't, though she doesn't tell him that. There's a particular sort of commitment which she craves.

Drifting in and out of sleep in the early morning, she dreams of her parents. It's a memory of them, as if she's heard their raised voices in the next room, the night-time bickering that always followed a day of cold disdain for each other.

She still plays her game. After two months of waitressing in a Spitalfields bistro, she's back in Paris, exhilarated again by the constant switching and shifting of destinations on the split-flap board. As she watches for one to catch her attention, her thoughts return to their last trip together. She remembers waking early in a Toulouse hotel, with a leak of sunlight where the curtains hadn't been quite closed, and easing herself into the curve of his back, knowing that they were under no pressure to get up, that they'd have coffee and eggs, and now there comes back to her something she read once. A relationship is made up of these small points of connection, brief empathetic highs that feed a sense of permanence, not a constant state that has to be maintained. If she could have held onto that thought, things might have turned out differently. But it's one thing to have flashes of insight, and another thing altogether to live by them when you feel the chemicals flowing in your brain and the reaction is so physical.

## What a Performance!
Emily Bullock

The engraver holds up the plaque. He polishes away his thumbprint before he lets go. She slips it into the striped plastic bag he's left out. He rests an elbow on the counter. An upside-down heart is tattooed on his upper arm; t-shirt rolled up to keep it on display.

He catches her looking, squeezes his muscles to make the heart pump. 'Usually get asked for fancy engravings,' he says. 'Angels. Poems. That sort of thing.'

She would have to twist her neck to read the upside-down name inked there. He tilts his head to one side, waiting for some reply. She does a half-raise-half-nod of her head; sometimes it's difficult to know what's expected.

She holds the rustling plastic close, takes a step away from the counter. The words won't come out. *My parents*. It strikes her for the first time now that she's an orphan; although at fifty-three she doesn't expect any sympathy. The engraver opens the till, slips in the note, drops the coins one by one. The aisle is narrow, if she turns too quickly she'll knock over the display of small silver golfers, sticks raised in the air. The till pings shut. She's nearly at the door. Un-won cups, blank first place shields line the shelves; a row of six-inch Jesus statues watch.

He calls out, louder than needed in that small shop, 'Into amateur dramatics, were they?'

She puts her hand on the warm glass of the door, and nods not because it's true but because she wants to be out of there.

He laughs. 'Knew it must be that.'

It must be nice to be so sure of things. The bell above the door rings like an alarm clock. But she's not late, there's no hurry. She's the only one left: no brothers or sisters. She blinks against the October light glinting off shop fronts. The breeze plucks at the plastic bag, flicking it against the brass plate inside; sounding like tapping fingers. The bench has been waiting years for its plaque, growing green and cracked. She can't help trotting along the High Street, heading towards the park, not wanting it to wait any longer.

She had been at work last week when the call came from the nursing home, saying her dad had died. That wooden bench had crept into her thoughts before she hung up the phone. He used to joke, 'I'm long past my sell-by date.' He would smile, tiny bird skull nodding against the plastic-covered chair. But on her last Saturday visit he grabbed her hand, dragged himself upright. He said, 'I've lived too long but there wasn't enough time.' He didn't look at her, his eyes were searching for someone else in that overheated dayroom.

The street is busy: teenagers in blue uniforms huddle round cones of chips; OAPs queue at bus stops, leaning on tartan shopping trolleys; seagulls circle the rooftops. She keeps close to the shops, careful not to get swept up in a rush for the pedestrian crossing. The striped plastic sticks to her palms; she forgot to bring a bag for life and this one cost her five pence. She'll have to carry her lunch in it, or line the bedside bin with it, but she'll still hear her mum's voice: Look after the pennies and the pounds will look after themselves. She can't throw it away; some sense of the sin of this lingers in her mouth like the metallic tang of licking a penny.

The green umbrella of the park opens above the end of the street. Just the lunchtime queue for the post office to get past. She holds the bag tight to her chest. But no one taps her on the shoulder, no one calls her name. Walking anywhere with her mum used to take an age, always stopping to chat with Church People, as her mum called them. It has been five years since her mum's funeral; the graveyard backs onto the park.

When she was seven, her mum gave her a plastic Jesus: heart open and bleeding. At night it went beat-beat-beat. Even the cool side of the pillow, dragged up around her ears, couldn't silence it. Next to it on the bedside table squatted the Union Jack moneybox from her dad. Inside the birthday card her mum had written: *Next Sunday we'll get Jesus blessed.*

The park gates are open, clanging church bells echo over the skateboard slopes and duck pond. The sun balances low on the branches. Plump toddlers swing in the play area; screaming with laughter, launching themselves down slides into the embrace of waiting arms. It's too late for all that, but she came close once. Although watching mothers wheeling prams, chasing scooters, she could never imagine herself doing that. So many children running, flapping their coats like wings as they see off pigeons. She turns left at the roses; clipped and netted down for the coming winter. Not far now.

The gardener starts a leaf-blower; spluttering gas, sneezing out dust. It looks like someone has used a mower to cut his grey hair down low until there is nothing but new shoots on his head. The gardener bleeds the fuel line, blue smoke hangs heavy over the grass. It scratches at her nose, stings her eyes. She promised herself she wouldn't cry and she hasn't, not even yesterday at her dad's funeral.

It takes a moment to find the bench; smoke from burning leaves drifts across the path. The air is heavy as wet wool. Her boots crunch over the remains of a bottle as she sits down. She can't quite bring herself to let go of the bag yet, it rests on her lap.

Her parents smiled and held hands when they told her they had put money aside for a bench in the local park, and there were detailed instructions about the brass plaque they wanted attached. They had presumed they would die together – something dramatic like a coach crash – flash of flames and back to ash. When it didn't happen that way her dad wouldn't let her attach the plaque or tell her what it was to say; he left the wording and a cheque with his papers at the care home. In that dry cleaning box stuffed with memories she found the plastic Jesus her mum gave her, or rather what was left of it. It met with an accident before it even got blessed: leaning too close to a 40 watt bulb. Red cloak melted into a blob, tiny heart inflated like a balloon.

She leans back on the bench, angled towards the fading sun. Five years the bench has been waiting for this dedication. She visits most lunch breaks; only a short walk, and two roads to cross, from the doctor's surgery where she's practice manager.

A car horn blares, brakes squeal, sending starlings spiralling and chattering into the sky. Bang. The leaf-blower hits tarmac. The gardener cuts the engine. She opens the bag, runs her finger over the engraving. Perhaps she should have brought a poem, something fitting to say. But she's never really been one for such displays. Instead she closes her eyes, takes a moment to remember.

That catholic girl, that protestant boy. The chances of her parents meeting seems less likely than the chances of plastic Jesus healing himself. 'It's my right to marry who I please,' Dad would say. 'It's my penance,' Mum would say and she said it a lot, the other favourite was, 'Jesus, Mary and Joseph... One day...' Whatever that threat was it never got said. But there were other times when arguments would boil over like Horlicks left too long in the pan: smoking, leaving a sharp burning taste in the mouth, and tight skin on top.

Here's a memory... A shard of glass lay wedged against the refrigerator, beside it another and another. The milk draining across the sloping lino, losing itself beneath the skirting board.

'It'll be a cold day in hell before I clear up after you, Billy,' Mum said.

Dad shrugged; trying not to limp in his milk-soaked socks. He turned quickly at the back door – hoping to see Mum on bended knee, the dustpan in her hand? Mum stood with her hands on her hips.

He slammed the door, the glass in the kitchen window shook. Shoeless, Dad crunched across the gravel. Mum slammed the front room door. Their arguments could fill the air like a gas leak; any brush of static could explode it. A stale smell of tobacco came through the window. And out in the shed, the red-tipped glow of a roll-up inflated and deflated like a tiny beating plastic heart.

It took nearly ten years for the milk bottle shards to be absorbed by the orange lino. She'd moved out of home by then but on visits there was still the hallway of no man's land to negotiate; the sideboard presided over by the Pope and the Holy Mother in hologram, and the shed with the Union Jack flag and the Diana wedding mug. It was about that time Mum sat down in the wingback chair, the tapestry covered one by the window. And that was it, she never cooked another meal, never made another cup of tea.

Dad played his part; storing ammunition for whenever there was a witness in the room. 'Tell her what you told me this morning, Theresa?'

'Such a fuss, Billy. All I said was, *They've opened a new sex shop in the precinct.*'

'Tell her what they do at that sex shop of yours?'

'These are modern times! What's wrong with men and women getting seen to in the same place?'

'Unisex! She means unisex hairdressers.' Dad handed over Mum's lunch as if it was a reward. 'Dogs in the street know more than you do.'

He stopped using a plate, loading her food onto a plastic tray. Each Jacobs Cream Cracker picked up, each crumbling cracker topped with a slice of cheddar and Granny Smith, revealed a little more of the design beneath. Mum always left one denture-sized bite to make sure the Queen's face never got uncovered. But how they pined for coddle, colcannon, potatoes boiled so long all the starch floated out. They both grew thin and transparent as newspaper left in the rain.

The wooden bench is soft from all the rain they've been having. She's brought a mini screwdriver, the screws start to bite. Splinters of wood poke into her fingers.

The plaque is in place. All is quiet. Shadows from tall pines stretch towards the bench, deepening the engraved words:

*What a Performance!*

Maybe her life will always be as an understudy: false starts, run-throughs without applause. So busy watching from the wings, she missed her entrance. But the shadow isn't the trees. The gardener stands in front of the bench.

He points at the plaque, asks, 'A joke or a warning?'

'A statement.'

He nods. 'Never been much into them.'

She does that thing again, half eyebrow raise, half nod. But he doesn't leave, he straightens his overalls. Council Amenity Maintenance Worker printed on the top pocket. No maintenance worker ever eased daffodil buds from cracked frost or mulched leaves to blanket roses. She's seen him bedding chrysanthemums too.

'Show's over,' he says, brushing dust from his arms, moving towards the grass. 'I've seen you here before. Like this bench, do you?'

She likes milk cartons that don't shatter, Monet prints on the wall, eating dinner off a plate. Up ahead a street lamp flickers yellow, frost crystallizing on shaded stretches of tarmac. The sunset burns bright, reflected off the bronze plate.

She stands up. 'It's a good spot for lunch.'

The gardener pushes a clump of grass into place with his boot. 'Then I'll start bringing my sandwiches here.' He turns, waves over his shoulder, returns to the leaf blower.

Maybe tomorrow's matinee will be different.

## This England
Oscar Windsor-Smith

I wish Felix was here. I miss him so much.

Tugging at my brother's sleeve, I whisper, 'Felix would like to see the trees whiz by, wouldn't he, Jack?'

Jack nods. I miss Mummy and Daddy, too.

'Mummy and Daddy would love to see the trees and the fields whizzing by, wouldn't they, Jack?'

Jack nods again. He's turned his head away as if he's looking out of the window, but I think he's pretending.

Miriam is sitting next to Jack. Jack is holding her hand. She looks scared, but she's only little. Miriam is seven, a whole year younger than me.

With his other hand, Jack is twisting the brown label hanging on string around his neck. I think he's feeling sad.

Miriam is sniffling. She wipes her nose on the sleeve of her coat. She says, 'I want Mummy,' and starts crying again.

'Would Felix be able to see out of the window? If he was sitting on the train seat like us, would he be able to see the trees? Jack?'

Jack lets go of Miriam's hand and stands up. Jack is really big. He's ten and he's taller even than the middle of the train door where the leather belt is that works the window.

Jack takes hold of the belt and pulls it and the window opens – crash – and the carriage is full of smelly smoke and diddledy-dum noises coming from the wheels and woosh-woosh sounds every time a telegraph pole flashes by.

'Why couldn't we bring Felix with us, Jack?'

Jack leans forward with his elbows on the window. He's looking out, hair blowing in the wind. When he turns back to me I think he must have got smoke in his eyes because they're all watery.

'Felix was only a cat, Alec. We're together, that's all that matters now.

'You mean Felix is a cat, Jack.'

'Yes, that's what I meant.'

'When will Mummy and Daddy come?'

Jack leans out of the window again. He's making a sound as if he's laughing, but I don't think he is.

Miriam is crying louder. 'I want Mummy and Daddy.'

Jack takes a deep breath and steps back from the window. He blows his nose, looks at Miriam and me and says, 'Let's play a game?'

'Yes, let's play.'

'Will you play, too, Miriam?' Jack says.

Miriam has stopped crying. She rolls out her bottom lip like when she's sulking and then she nods, slowly.

'What shall we play, Jack?'

'We're going to play Angels and Scary Goblins.'

Miriam is smiling. She claps her hands. 'I want to be a Scary Goblin,' she shouts.

'No. Me. Me. Me. I'm a Scary Goblin.'

'That's not how we play it,' Jack says, pointing out of the window at the blue sky. 'Look up there.'

When I screw up my eyes against the bright light I can see little dots twisting and turning. They're writing chalk-marks on the sky.

'Some of them are Angels and some are Scary Goblins,' says Jack. 'We've got to guess which are which and who is going to win.'

I know Jack is pretending for Miriam. Those aren't really Angels and Scary Goblins, they're aeroplanes. When they dive lower I can see circles on the wings of some and black crosses on the wings of others.

Jack gets Miriam to hold up all her fingers. She's laughing now. 'When I say Scary Goblin you put down one of these fingers,' he says, tickling her under the arm and making her squeal. 'And when Alec says Angel you put down one of these fingers.' He tickles her under the other arm.

And then my big brother Jack puts his arms around us both. We laugh and shout as loud as we can at the Angels and Scary Goblins until the train whistle blows.

'We're coming to a station,' Jack says. He stands on the seat to lift our cases down from the rack. And then he takes a clean handkerchief from his pocket and wipes Miriam's eyes and makes her blow her nose.

The train has stopped. People are running up and down the platform looking into the windows. A lady opens our door. She's waving and pointing at Jack, Miriam and me and saying words I don't understand. Standing behind the lady is a man in black uniform with shiny silver badges and a big hat. Looking fierce, he reaches in and takes hold of Jack's label. The man nods. He says something to the lady and they both laugh.

The woman and the man move aside, pushing another man, dressed in a greenish-brown uniform, towards us. He steps forward, points to the lady and then to us. He speaks slowly. His words are very strange.

'To England and your new family you are most welcomed,' he says, and smiles.

For more information on the kindertransport:
https://encyclopedia.ushmm.org/content/en/article/kindertransport-1938-40

## My Daddy
Carolyn Eden

My daddy can't come to parents' evening because he's stuck up in the sky, on the Space Station making solar-powered magnets so that no one will ever feel cold again.

My daddy can't watch me run at Sports Day because he's had to dash over to France, to coach Real Barcelona for the football championship this summer.

No, my daddy won't be in the audience at the Carol Concert because he's a secret agent and has been sent to spy on Chinese munitions factories. We might have to move to a safe house any time now and change our identities and I'll have to have my hair cut really short and wear big sunglasses like my mum. They'll find it hard to get the right actor to play my daddy when they make a film of it because he's so good looking.

My daddy can't come to the end of term play because secretly he's really a King in a big country, and has sent me here so that I can grow up among the common people, without airs and graces. He usually comes to see me in disguise, but this year he has to go and help his poorer people who got caught up in a flood.

*

Some people have been saying things about Daddy that aren't true. Mum says that I should take no notice, and that when I am older I will understand, and that she's sorry she has to go to work all day and can't walk me to school any more. Lots of other children don't even have daddies anymore, or have to live in different houses or with their nanas.

It is not true that my daddy sometimes cries for no reason. My daddy never forgets to wash and he shaves every day even when he doesn't have to go out.

My daddy doesn't stand for hours at the front door breathing like he's going to dive from the highest board at the swimming pool. He doesn't eat slowly and never spills the water because his hands are shaky.

*

My daddy will come to pick me up one day very soon in a big shiny car with tinted windows, and you'll see how handsome he is, like the prince in the pantomime that our mummies took us to see at the theatre on Boxing Day. And my daddy will bring me lots of presents from his adventures and build a tree house for me, and push me on the swings and wait at the bottom of the curly-wurly slide, where you sit inside the tube, and swish round the bend and it's all dark and you feel all shivery, until you see a trickle of light, like the hole my daddy made for me in the cardboard box, so I could look at the eclipse... only we didn't see, because it was cloudy over our house.

I wish it wasn't always so cloudy.

My daddy is busy mapping the Amazon River next week.

*

This week my daddy has to help the doctors again with their cure for agri-culture. I don't know what that is, but it's very important.

*

Lots of things have changed. We open the curtains downstairs on Saturday mornings now. Daddy helps me with my spellings and tests me on my times-tables and reads me a story every night at bedtime.

*

Mum is ever so pleased that Daddy has fixed the washing machine all by himself, because it's just a clogged up thing and my mummy should have checked the pockets better, and he's found my lucky whistle my nana gave me in there, and Mum didn't cry, even though he seemed cross.

*

Nana left us last year, it made Daddy very sad, I think because she had wanted to come on holiday with us, and Mum said no, we needed a break just us, because I was going to have a little brother or sister, and Nana was cross. Only I didn't get a little brother or sister. And when Daddy went round to see her after we got back, Nana had gone.

*

Daddy cooked our dinner last night and it was spaghetti and we all got messy and laughed and then I had to have a bath. Later Daddy went to the 'never-touch-anything-on-the-desk' room and I know he didn't play on his computer, because there were no Candy Crush ponging noises, just little clip-clacks.

*

Mum is pleased 'cause I have been ever-so-helpful lately, and stood quietly by the back door as we've done breathing all together, and I've told jokes and shared my pick-and-mix bags with Daddy, and pretended not to mind that I have to walk home from school on my own. And everything will be ok, because Mum and Daddy love me very much, and they hold hands during the scary parts of Dr Who, which I don't understand, but I like to be able to talk about the monsters in the playground on Monday mornings.

*

To go home on my own I have to turn left (that's watch-hand left) and walk straight down and cross by the traffic lights. Then I have to turn right (that's the hand with grazed knuckles from tripping over I-told-you-so shoelaces).

*

Mum is standing at our front garden gate. She's smiling. She's wearing the dress with yellow flowers that reminds me of picnics on the big hill in the park where the giraffes live.

He's there, standing at the front door, waiting for me. Then he's taking one, two, three, four steps past my first-Christmas tree that grew and grew.

He's at the gate now, holding Mum's hand like I used to, when I was really little and too scared to walk past the bicycle racks at baby school. His skin is so pale and he is waving at me.

I run towards him like a stone from a naughty boy's catapault. He smells of lemons and peppermint. Mum laughs out loud because we, me and Daddy, are both rubbing grit from our eyes.

## Departures
Liam Hogan

Two men meet in an airport departure lounge. One, travelling West, wears a dark charcoal suit and even in the airport thinks he represents his company, as he has not even loosened his thin, neutrally coloured tie.

The other wears loose-fitting trousers and a pair of shoes that would be turned away at most nightclubs. He carries a canvas backpack that looks like it's been round the world a few times.

It has.

There is little reason for the two of them to converse, except that the lounge is otherwise empty. It is between planes; the man in the suit arrived an hour earlier than he needed to, worried about missing his flight, whereas the man with the canvas bag cut his departure customarily fine, and – the airline having over-booked – has waived his seat in return for an upgrade on a later flight. His eyes dart around the room, with the look of a man who is... well, what? Hunted? Or haunted?

'You're going to Milan?' he asks the suit.

The suit... no. Let's call him Mr West, and the other, Mr East, these men – like all men in departure lounges – have no names.

West, then, looks up with surprise. 'Well yes. How did you know?'

'MXP,' East says, pointing at the baggage sticker on the back of the other's flight ticket. 'Malpensa. I know all the airport codes.'

West takes this in. He blinks. But he is polite and a conversation has been started. 'And you? Where are you heading?'

'East,' says East. 'I'm heading... East.' An odd comment, and West thinks that this probably concludes his obligation, but East has one more variation to add: 'Always East.'

'Always East?' echoes West, and at this East nods fervently.

'Always East,' he says with emphasis.

West shifts uncomfortably in his seat, and can't think what to say. 'Never West?'

'Never,' affirms East.

'But how do you get home?' West asks.

East shrugs. 'I don't. I've been heading East for seventeen years.'

West is confused. 'But...'

'It's my fortune you see,' says East, but no, West does not see, and the blank look he gives is answer enough.

East quickly glances around the still quiet room. A few other passengers have wandered in and have spread themselves to the points of the compass, avoiding the already occupied centre. 'When I was young,' he says, 'a fortune teller told me to go East. *Go East,* she said, *and you will become a millionaire.*' He rubs his neck. 'The problem is you carry East and West around with you. Even now, you are on my East side, and I, on your West. I can go East until I'm back where I started and then keep on going. And I have. East without end, always chased, never caught.'

West sits up straighter. He thinks of himself as a rational man and he doesn't believe in fortune tellers any more than he believes in the Tooth Fairy, or in Father Christmas. 'How do you know that this is not a false fortune?' he asks.

East holds his eye for a long moment and then nods firmly.

'I know.' And this is enough for both of them, because it is obviously a matter of faith and you don't question a man's faith.

West turns instead to matters of a more practical nature.

'How do you afford it?' he asks.

East smiles. 'I work. I travel as far East as I can, then I stop and work until I have enough to move on.'

West smiles in return. 'You know,' he says gently, 'the average person earns around a million dollars in their lifetime. More perhaps. Much more, if it's in Hong Kong dollars, or Yen. Have you never thought of just staying where you land, of settling?'

East twitches. His wrings his hands together to still their betrayal. 'How can I?' he says, a hint of mournful despair in his voice. 'Once you start... once you have invested so much... to give up now–' His tortured reply is interrupted by a garbled tannoy announcement. 'My flight,' East says, though he makes no immediate move to stand. Then he speaks again, a wild rush of words: 'And... and that was only half of the future she told me! If it was only about money!' he says. 'The rest... and I have not told this to many people... the rest was *and there you will find love, and happiness, and peace.*"

There is little West can say. He is sceptical, of course. How could an itinerant traveller, who never stays anywhere long enough to do more than scrape together an air ticket, ever hope to find his fortune? What a miracle it would require! But he nods and says 'I hope you find what you are looking for.' They shake hands and as East hefts his bag a half dozen business cards rain down from a side pocket. West stoops to pick them up, but East shakes his head. 'They are of no use to me anymore. Leave them be.' And with that he is striding towards the gate.

After he has gone, West sits staring at nothing awhile, before he checks his watch, and – seeing he has just enough time – hurriedly pulls out his laptop. Emblazoned with the logo of the travel company he works for, he opens it and enters the name from one of the spilled business cards. And there it is, confirmation. Page after page of entries, from check-in desks in every country on every continent, mark the ever eastward journey, circling the globe over and over and over.

And something more as well; a dozen different loyalty card schemes with a dozen different airlines. He sucks at the tip of a pencil and quickly jots down numbers – BA, Virgin Flying Club, Flyer Plus, before adding them up.

He leans back in his chair and grins, catching the eye of a matronly lady who has just sat down and who looks initially scandalised, and then scowls back. But that just makes West grin even more.

Because whatever his next flight, whoever it is with, it will take Mr East over that magic seven digit number. By the time he lands, he'll be a million-air-miler.

West sends him all of the joy he can muster, and snaps his laptop shut.

## Alpaca Moonlight
V G Lee


'I am not a lesbian,' Deirdre sang in a high but surprisingly tuneful voice. 'But I'm open to temptation.'

'What, you're bi-curious?' I asked.

'Dude, I'd rather eat my own foot than get close up and personal with another woman.' She looked thoughtful then said, 'I'm not that keen on getting close up and personal with my Martin either, bless his smelly socks!'

It was a warm afternoon in summer and I was sitting in Deirdre's garden which is small but raised to give a very distant sea view. (Deirdre insists the sea view adds at least another twenty thousand to the value of her small terraced house.) I half-lay, half-lounged on one of her new hard-wood recliners trying to ignore the clank of metal colanders painted in seaside colours that she'd welded into an enormous wind chime and hung from one of the skeletal branches of her dead Acer. I do admire Deirdre's ability to turn her hand to welding even if she has left large deposits of weld on her fitted carpets – that at a glance can easily be mistaken for Lord Dudley's (Deirdre's high-maintenance cat) misdemeanours.

'It isn't dead,' she insisted re the Acer, not Lord Dudley. 'It's in a state of cryonic hibernation.' She'd followed this statement with rapidly blinking her eyes and instantly I'd known that she was quoting something Martin had told her.

I tapped the nearest colander with my index finger, just enough to set the whole edifice moving. A flake of aquamarine paint spiralled down onto the decking. We both stared at it.

With the toe of one faded blue bootee, Deirdre nudged the flake till it disappeared down a crack between the boards, into the hollow area where once the koi carp pond had been.

'I'm off to London tomorrow,' I said. 'A book launch at Foyles.'

'Foyles? Is that like… Bluewater?' She bundled her sheaf of curly hair onto the top of her head and secured it with some garden twine.

'No. It's a big bookshop covering several floors. The author is Elfrida Greenlawne. She's a notable feminist lesbian.'

'Never heard of her.' Deirdre adopted the sneer in both tone and facial expression she only adopts when talking about poor people, ugly people, smelly people and almost anyone who belongs to or works in a library.

I persevered. 'Her writing is a bit like Sarah Waters' only more rural.'

'Never heard of her either. What about Dan Brown? I've heard of him.'

'He's not a feminist lesbian.'

'Your point being?' Deirdre said.


We hadn't been getting on since the evening I'd announced that I wanted to be a more visible lesbian and not just her best friend. Deirdre had looked up from unwrapping a Cadbury Creme Egg and said, 'What's wrong with being my best friend?'

'Nothing at all. But you have Martin and Lord Dudley. It's only natural that I should want a woman to share my life with.'

'It doesn't seem natural to me.'

'That's because you're straight,' I said.

Deirdre answered, 'I am what I am,' but she'd looked offended.


Back in Deirdre's garden, she began to spray the foxgloves growing between the paving stones with weed killer.

I said, 'Foxgloves are wild flowers not weeds.'

'Well, they're dead wild flowers now. I'll meet you at the bookshop.'

'But you don't know where it is.'

'Then tell me. It's no big deal, is it?'

And yet it was quite a big deal. Deirdre was perfectly at home in M&S, Debenhams and Evans Outsize. Perfectly at home in Born-to-Dye-Young where she had her blonde highlights enhanced each month, but Deirdre in London, in a bookshop, surrounded by shelves of just... books, that was well outside her comfort zone.

I reached Foyles with at least an hour to spare. Ray's Jazz Café was crowded and smelt of wet coats. I settled myself with a coffee and the Evening Standard on a stool near the window. Under the guise of puzzling over crossword clues I glanced around the room trying to pick out obvious lesbians maybe waiting like myself for the reading, but no, I was the only obvious lesbian.

I'd aimed for a 'womb to womanhood' look. Under normal circumstances I wear a bra, but no bra that evening. 'Let it all hang loose', I'd told myself as I'd towelled dry after a shower, but just in case it was all hanging a little too loosely, I'd added several concealing layers of pea-green: vest, large t-shirt followed by gigantic knitted cardigan. My baggy trousers were held up with a leather belt, I hoped this combined lesbian chic with artisan credibility. In my pockets I'd stuffed clean handkerchiefs, a tube of peppermints, gum, should I need to chew nervously (yet carelessly), a big bunch of keys to jingle carelessly (yet quietly) – the key ring bearing an image of a semi-nude Ann Bannon heroine – much loose change, and a pearl-handled pen-knife with several useful attachments that in my twenty-year ownership I'd never felt the need to utilise.

Finishing my coffee, I took the stairs up to Silver Moon, on the third floor. Four rows of chairs were arranged in a semi-circle. On a small table, copies of Elfrida Greenlawne's new novel *Alpaca Moonlight* were stacked next to a black and white photograph of the author hugging a sheep.

I sat down in the back row as the all-female audience began to drift in. Hungrily, I watched the women. Here was a club that I didn't yet belong to. Several women browsed the shelves. Why hadn't I browsed the shelves? What could be more natural than a lesbian browsing a shelf of lesbian literature?

An excited murmur ran through the audience as a large woman wearing a flower-patterned kaftan and royal blue suede bootees, carrying several John Lewis carrier bags, made her way determinedly towards the woman organising the event.

The woman next to me whispered, 'That must be Elfrida Greenlawne. She looks nothing like her photograph.'

'Actually, that's my friend, Deirdre,' I said.

The organiser had made the same mistake. Holding out her hand, she advanced on Deirdre. 'Thank you so much for coming all the way from your small-holding in the shadow of the Malvern Hills.'

Deirdre ignored her. Like an embattled wild animal, she glared fiercely at the audience.

I stood up and waved, 'Deirdre, over here.'

She picked up the chair put out for Elfrida Greenlawne and carried it shoulder high to where I was sitting in the back row.

'Budge up so I can get this chair in next to my friend?' Deirdre told the woman sitting next to me.

'There's not enough room.'

'Of course there is. Just budge up.'

Reluctantly the woman budged up.

Elfrida Greenlawne looked exactly like her photograph minus the sheep. She wore a large pullover, faded cotton trousers and muddy boots. Her hair was admirably wild, tangled and tawny.

Deirdre hissed, 'That woman's not been near a comb in decades.'

Thirty minutes later, I was on my feet, clapping and cheering. My mind was full of possibilities that had never occurred to me before. Should I go on a fell walking holiday? Could I sunbathe topless and swim in icy rock pools? Was it too late to take up kick-boxing, bee-keeping, plant husbandry?

I turned to Deirdre to say, 'Wasn't she great?' but she was already several feet away picking up a book from a display of...

Deirdre flipped the book open in the middle. 'Eeugh! Gross! Dude, I'm bringing up my breakfast.'

...lesbian erotica.

She tossed it back on the shelf. Head on one side she began to read out book titles, 'Hot Lesbian Erotica, Best Lesbian Bondage Erotica, Vampire Erotica, Five-minute Erotica –'

'Deirdre!'

'The Mammoth Encyclopaedia of Erotica, The Golden Age of Lesbian Erotica – don't you lesbians have any other interests?'

'It's a display of lesbian erotica.'

'It's not for me, dude. I'll meet you in Pizza Hut.'

I bought my signed copy of *Alpaca Moonlight* and set off after her. By the time I reached Pizza Hut, she'd already filled her bowl from the salad bar and one for me too – heavy on the croutons the way Deirdre knows I like.

I sat down.

She speared a tiny tomato and popped it in her mouth before asking, 'Do lezzers become lezzers because they're ugly? Or does growing ugly come with the lezzer territory?'

'Excuse me, Deirdre, but lesbians are no uglier than straight people.'

'Two cokes,' Deirdre told the waitress. 'No ice. I've ordered our pizzas. Fancy swapping half yours for half mine?'

'No,' I snapped.

'Oh-oh, there's one now – it's the woman who didn't want to budge up. Is there some sort of dress code? Wear anything that nobody in their right mind would want to wear and by the way pea-green's not your colour – you look as if you're coming down with gastric flu.'

'Hello again,' the woman said hesitating at our table. 'Elfrida Greenlawne was terrific, wasn't she?'

'She was shite,' Deirdre said. I kicked her under the table. 'A total loser. Small-holding in the shadow of the Malvern Hills... my arse. What she needs,' Deirdre stabbed a quarter of hard-boiled egg, 'is for some big hairy bloke to give her a good shagging.' She looked at me, 'And you can stop kicking me under the table because this is a free country and I'm entitled to my opinion.'

Two Deirdre-less years passed. I found a girlfriend. We went on a fell walking holiday and I bathed in an icy rock pool and came down with pleurisy. While recovering, my girlfriend met someone else. I joined a kick-boxing class, but may never go topless or keep bees. During all this activity I didn't once glimpse Deirdre – not even a sighting in Born-to-Dye-Young having her highlights highlighted. And then one morning, just before nine, my bus was stuck in traffic on the High Street. I noticed that Marks & Spencer was having a summer sale. Their double doors were still locked but a large blonde-haired woman was ramming the glass with her shoulder. Inside the store a sales assistant was shaking her head and pointing at her watch.

Deirdre – of course it had to be Deirdre – took a step backwards. I thought she was about to walk away but instead she bellowed, 'Dude, will you open this fucking door?'

The next day, I took the train to London. My first stop was Foyles. I climbed the stairs to the third floor and stood in the place I judged Silver Moon Books had once been. It is now called the GLBT section and is full of light whereas Silver Moon seemed quite dark which is how I feel a good bookshop should seem. I stared down at the wood block floor and mused that maybe it used to be carpeted and that the carpet once carried an impression of Deirdre's booted feet coming down hard, summoning up every bit of her courage, carrying chair and John Lewis carrier bags towards me through the rows of women so unlike herself. I remembered thinking that she'd looked like an embattled wild animal. Yes, Deirdre was rude, homophobic, and could be thoroughly nasty, but what sort of friend had I been? I'd never given a thought to how she was feeling, not just then, but from the moment I'd told her being her best friend just wasn't enough.

Leaving Foyles, I headed for Oxford Street and Deirdre's spiritual home – the bed linen department in John Lewis. I've always been drawn to anything floral and at that moment I felt I desperately needed a floral hit. And there it was. Perfect. Egyptian cotton, 600 threads, pink tea roses.

In my head I seemed to hear Deirdre's voice. 'Step away from that bedding.'

My hand reached out to pluck the duvet set from the shelf. 'Leave it!'

The voice was at my shoulder. I turned. 'Deirdre?'

She held up her hand, 'Love means never having to say you're sorry.'

'I wasn't intending to say sorry,' I replied rather stiffly.

'Me neither.'

'Did you get my letter?' I asked.

'I did, but you know how I hate words on paper. Could be dyslexia, could be a neurosis. Martin gave it the once-over and said you'd been stuck between a rock and a hard place.'

Deirdre looked different. Her hair was short, her thick golden curls fitting close to her head, which somehow made her face look thoughtful yet animated rather than tempestuous and over-excitable. Her clothes were different too, less flamboyant; a linen trouser suit, the loose jacket with an unexpected but stylish Nehru collar.

She met my gaze and grinned, 'Guess what? I'm a feminist

now, as in,' she held her telescopic umbrella in front of her face as if it was a microphone, 'I am strong,' she sang, 'I am invincible. Love that word "invincible". Who'd have thought someone would stick it in a lyric? Martin says whoever it was should publish a book on how to write a blockbuster hit.'

It was as if there'd been no break in our friendship, as if those times when we'd had nothing kind or nice to say to each other had never been. I returned the duvet set to the shelf. By unspoken mutual agreement we set off in search of a cafeteria. Standing side by side on the escalator heading upwards, Deirdre said, 'I saw you once in that bookshop. You were buying an arm-load of books. Afterwards I went up to the assistant and said, 'I'll take whatever that woman in the pea-green cardigan bought.'

## Cloud Island
Cherry Potts


The first thing you notice is the slight springiness underfoot, the sway and bounce of all those other feet, somewhere ahead of you, reverberating and rustling through the woven structure.

You hesitate, never that fond of bridges, never that fond of heights and although well rooted, this bridge is high, and you wonder about its well-routed-ness, where are we all going, after all?

Of course you've heard all about how strong and waterproof the living bamboo can be, but the only times you've laid your hand to bamboo, it has been dead, long cut and brittle, and when put under enough pressure, disintegrating into splinters and sharp shards as it splits and snaps.

But this – this is still growing, it flexes and bounces and shifts one stem against another as it accommodates all those feet – so many – all those travellers to somewhere else.

It makes you uneasy, this warped and twisted living thing, as espaliered fruit trees do, and bonsai. It is not natural, is it, to torture growing things like this, to force them out of their preferred habit to suit our purpose.

But you like the structure itself, there is something ancient about it, that reminds you of the rush barges of the Nile, of the sun boat that Ra steers across the heavens. Where does this sun bridge across the sky steer us?

The bridge artists weave the still growing stalks into archways and trellis, sculptures and pergolas. They have to work fast, the bamboo grows faster than they can imagine new structures, and in places thickets grow so thick they have to work constantly to keep the pathways clear. There is already a third tier of walkways; balconies and tea houses sprout on every side.

Who would have thought the bamboo would respond so well to its new growth habit?

Insects rustle in the darkness. You would not consider this crossing in anything but full daylight even though hordes of lamp sellers and guides pull at your sleeve. Lanterns are carved from complete sections of the giant bamboo, and carried on gracefully bending poles so that parties of travellers cross the dark like shoals of anglerfish trawling for unwary small fry.

In daylight the whole structure is alive with birds and butterflies and innocent lizards as green as the new leaf, or as golden as the wood, flitting between pillars of living wicker. Bright feathers and brighter voices, and far, far below, the humdrum world. Who would not want to shed their cares and walk here a while?

And there is the constant sweet sound of stems rubbing together, and the wind sighing through the leaves, and the chink of china bowls from the tea houses, and the murmur of polite greeting and the persistent *Madam, Madam* of the bridge dwellers, offering all kinds of souvenirs, all made from bamboo, of course.

And there is the art – not just the sculpture, but exquisite scenes carved into the living wood, some of the older ones distorted and made grotesque by passing time and growth, so that the once beautiful goddess on her cloud island is gross and hideous, her body twisted and her face deformed into a leering monster. You shy away from that, what a wonderful lesson in what comes to us all.

And then, there is the smell. The acid sharp of fresh growth, and the muddy, dead smell of rot from the lower levels. Where the oldest branches are they grow in complete darkness, and everything everyone drops, biscuit crumbs, sugared almonds, jade earrings, gold; falls through the woven surface to lie and fester and provide nutrients for the young growth, and the cockroaches.

You want to go barefoot, to experience that swaying bowing

spring fully, but you are afraid of being bitten by the rats which make their nests in the underbelly.

*Madam, Madam.*

Now you are offered felt slippers that flex to the living growth more naturally than your stiff-soled sandals, and at last you step up and join the constant, but not excessive stream of voyagers, setting out – but in search of what?

Dreams, hopes, destinies, all are carried here in the hearts and minds of silken dandies lost in too much opium, earnest scholars, warriors in search of a challenge, sages after enlightenment.

And you? Where do you hope this bridge will take you?

*Madam, Madam* – you have not completed the destination on your visa, and so this earnest, unworthy, humble official, cannot apply his sigil, he cannot affix his black wax seal, cannot permit you to take one further step onto the bridge of uncertainty.

His brush is full of ink, eager, waiting, wanting you to be able to continue your journey, your pilgrimage, your quest?

*Ah yes, Madam, of course.*

He is satisfied. He offers a lantern, just in case.

## The Reigning Miss Morocco
Nicholas Ridley

Unlikely as it might seem, I was once engaged to the reigning Miss Morocco. It's a story I like to tell whenever I'm given the opportunity. I usually open by saying – a little ungallantly – that the competition hadn't been staged for several years. Nonetheless, being once engaged to the reigning Miss Morocco isn't something everyone can claim. What's more – most improbably – it has the merit of being true. Or that was what I believed at the time.

There wasn't any doubt that Lucette was the reigning Miss Morocco. She had the proof. Sitting in the candlelight, side by side, on the narrow bed in my barely-furnished room in the Passage Lacépède, we leafed through her album of photographs with a certain reverence. Sparkling tiaras, shining smiles, stilettos and swimsuits.

Whether or not we were ever engaged is a little more ambiguous.

My working days in Casablanca were not demanding. An hour or two of light teaching in the morning would be followed by a simple lunch at a food stall in the medina and a return to the villa that I shared with two other teachers in Casablanca's Jewish quarter. There, reclining on rush mats in our stone courtyard, we smoked *kif* in almond pipes under the branches of the fig tree and the jacaranda until it was time to return to the language school that employed us to teach English to a mix of native Moroccans and pieds-noirs.

On Tuesdays and Thursdays I taught my beginners class. They were a charming group, or so it seemed to me, the afternoon's *kif* having had a mellowing effect on my view of the world and everything in it.

For the first week or two it was a largish class in a smallish classroom, but this, too, might have been the effect of the *kif*. After that, the class grew noticeably smaller although the classroom itself remained the same size. With a reduced number of students, I was able to identify them more easily.

Fatima    Lucette

Fawzi                    Latifa

Hasan                              Giselle

Abdulaziz                                   Benoît

For the first hour of every lesson I loved them all unconditionally, and if, during the second hour, I loved them less and my patience became strained, I would only have to remind myself of the hideous linguistic complexities that face the foreign learner of English to regain my composure. By the end of each lesson, I was fairly certain we were friends again.

I was aware of her, of course. How could I not be? Lucette was in her late twenties, a *pied-noir* of Spanish extraction with large dark eyes, a mass of black hair, a wide smile and – during our lessons at least – a charmingly puzzled expression. Yes, I was aware of her, and more aware of her as class numbers dwindled, but nothing more than that.

Fawzi    Lucette

Hasan                    Latifa

Abdulaziz                              Benoît

One Tuesday, at the end of the lesson, Lucette stayed behind. A tricky point of grammar to be explained? A muddled example to be clarified? I rather doubted if I would be able to provide her with a satisfactory answer but I smiled encouragingly. Would I like her, she asked, standing close in front of me – red lips, perfect teeth, pale apricot skin – to give me a lift home? (Her question was, of course, in French. We wouldn't be attempting anything like this in English until the end of the book … if we ever reached the end, that is.) I thanked her kindly but declined for no better reason than, in the evening, I enjoyed walking home through the medina.

Next Thursday she asked me again. Again I declined. I'm not quite sure why but, at the time, it seemed the right thing to do.

The Tuesday after that Lucette didn't come to the class and neither did Abdulaziz. I didn't expect to see either of them again. It was therefore a surprise to find her sitting in her place the following Thursday (Abdulaziz never did reappear). When she approached me at the end of the lesson, I was ready. Her smile was as wide as ever but more determined. Would I, she asked me, refuse her offer again? She wasn't used to being refused, she said, but she would ask me this one last time. No, I said, I would not refuse her offer. I would be happy to accept and I meekly followed her to a smart yellow car parked illegally on the pavement outside the school.

The fact that she didn't ask me where I lived might have given me a clue that we weren't going there. Instead we headed out of town to the Corniche where, on a poor teacher's salary – and, as you may have gathered, I was, in every sense, a very poor teacher – it would never have occurred to me to go. After an astonishingly expensive meal at a very smart restaurant, where I might have felt distinctly uncomfortable if we hadn't had a private room or if I'd thought I might be paying, she put an arm round my neck, kissed me expertly and drove me home.

I'd expected she might be dismayed to discover where I lived but she seemed delighted to find that the Passage Lacépède was in such an unfamiliar quarter of the city. She instructed me to open the gates so that she could park her yellow car in the courtyard. We never normally unlocked the gates and I was worried that our fig tree might be damaged but Lucette didn't understand what I was saying. In any case, she wasn't a woman to be resisted.

The path of true love – if that's what it was – did not, and was never likely to, run smoothly. We spent very little time in each other's company and there was no question of our ever being seen together in public. Her family would not have approved of me. I couldn't blame them. Her brothers in particular would have been outraged. Should Francisco and Rodrigo become aware of our affair, said Lucette, they would certainly want to kill me. This seemed to me extreme, but I now understood why it was better that she parked her yellow car inside our courtyard and not outside our gate in the Passage Lacépède.

Our relationship was marked by squalls of rage and fractious jealousies although these could usually be resolved by candlelight. Our many misunderstandings – missed meetings, changed arrangements – were more tiresome. Some of them at least were caused by language problems. My French had improved but Lucette's English, very noticeably, had not, which irritated her considerably. Her solution was to impose a strict regime whereby we were permitted to speak French before we made love, but afterwards she would only speak to me in English. It may have been this that led me to believe we had become engaged. I'm not sure how it happened but, at the time, I was certain that this is what we'd agreed.

Later that night, watching her car turn the corner out of Passage Lacépède into Rue Lacépède, closing and locking the gates of the villa, lying in my single bed, blowing out the candle, I suppose I should have wondered how, at the end of the summer term, we were going to cope when I took her back with me to London, which is what, it seemed, we planned to do. She'd said something about living in Kensington and I'd promised her we would be better off in Belsize Park. I admit I didn't give it as much thought as I might have done, but I was young, pleasantly fatigued and confident that everything would work out in the end, which meant that night I slept as peacefully as I always did in Casablanca.

Fawzi   Latifa

Hasan                    Benoît

On the final Tuesday and Thursday of the summer term Lucette did not appear. This surprised and disappointed me. I wondered if it was the prospect of the end-of-term test that had frightened her. If it was, I felt this showed a lack of faith both in herself and in me. The end-of-term test wasn't something anyone in my class would be allowed to fail. On Tuesday I went through each of the questions several times, writing the answers on the whiteboard and ensuring that they had been copied down correctly. On Thursday Hasan, Fawzi, Latifa and Benoît all performed very commendably.

There was no way I could contact Lucette and it was very aggravating. I couldn't call her home. That would be inviting trouble. In any case, she had never given me her number. Usually I called her office but, each time I did, I was told she wasn't there. What could I do? We would be leaving for London soon. Time was running out and I was almost certain there were arrangements we ought to be making.

The term had finished. The school year was over. My time in Casablanca was coming to an end. We had packed our few belongings, said goodbye to our helpful neighbours in the brothel across the road and returned the keys of our villa to the landlord. My housemates and I would soon be going our separate ways.

I'd planned to spend my last night at a friend's flat in Rue Ibn Battuta. The next morning I would be flying to Algiers on the first stage of my journey home. Did I still believe that, in September, I would be sharing a bed-sit in Belsize Park with the reigning Miss Morocco? I may have done, although I'm not entirely sure. I'd been so occupied recently that I hadn't given it much thought. But now the time had come when I needed to know. To be clear what was happening.

Which is why, on my last evening, I find myself – where I have never been before – concealed in the bougainvillaea on the other side of the road from Lucette's family home in the Rue Constantine. I don't have long to wait. A two-seater sports car pulls up outside the front door. The horn is sounded. A moment later Lucette – looking particularly glamorous – is standing there in the street. I step out from behind the bougainvillaea.

—Good evening, I say to her in English.

She looks at me, puzzled. I don't know why this is. We covered 'formal greetings' in one of the first classes of the year.

—I'm going, she says.

This puzzles me until I realise that she wants to say she's going out.

—I'm going, too, I say.

I mean, of course, I'm going away and should perhaps have made this clearer.

Her expression of alarm is probably because she thinks I'm proposing joining her in the two-seater sports car. I step back and she is visibly relieved.

—I'm going to Algiers tomorrow, I say. Are you coming with me?

— ?

The driver – understandably – is becoming impatient.

—*Au revoir*, Nicolas, she says.

—Good bye, I say.

It is a sad little moment.

Returning through the wealthier suburbs, I tried to conjure in myself feelings of injury and betrayal but none would come. I kept to well-lit streets on the way to my friend's flat and doubled back several times. I was still mindful of Rodrigo and Francisco, but I knew now that I was no longer – if I had ever been – engaged to the reigning Miss Morocco.

## Animal with Moon
Barbara Renel


She steps aside to let them pass. A herd, four-legged, eyeless, earless. She hears their breath as they go by, feels the warmth of their bodies. The last waits for her and she rests her hand on its back as they walk together. They talk.

*We're moving on.*
Where are you going?
*We'll know when we get there.*
Can I come with you?
*You have your own path to follow.*
But I'm lost.
*Look for the landmarks.*

They continue together in silence.

The herd veers off into the field of moonlight. She watches as they graze. The last lifts its snout. Alert. Nosing the air. It catches the crescent moon on its head, like a juggler.

The animal is smiling.

## Through Security
Sarah Lawson


The taxi driver had known fares like this before, all flustered and nervous about getting to Heathrow on time.

'No worries,' he said. 'We'll make it, easy.'

'Oh good,' Connie said. She kept checking her passport and travel documents and looking out of the taxi window at the streets of west London. 'You drive this way a lot.'

'All the time,' said the taxi driver, a cheerful Jamaican.

'Terminal three,' the woman said.

'Right, no worries.'

Outside the car, Cromwell Road gave way to a faster clearway, then the Hammersmith Flyover, then an elevated stretch with an impressive view on both sides. Finally the road became a motorway and there weren't any more stoplights. There were big blue signs on the M4 pointing off to places you might want to go to if you weren't going to Heathrow.

'Goodness,' Connie said. 'It's a long way isn't it?' She added, 'Terminal three, you know.'

'Right, no worries,' the driver said.

There were slip roads going off to Slough and Windsor and all sorts of places. There was even a sign to a service area off to the left side, with a restaurant. Then a slip road to passenger terminals one, two, and three. Goodness, but it was a big place for just one airport! You didn't notice how big the whole place was when you were arriving. Then you just followed signs and didn't look around too much. You'd be anxious to get to wherever you were going.

At the departures bay she counted out the fare carefully. 'That's it, isn't it?' she said. 'The tip is included?'

'That's the total price, no extras. Special fare to airports.'

He lifted her suitcase out of the car boot in one easy motion. 'And here's your case. You got plenty of time. You have a good trip now!'

'Thanks,' she said, relaxing a bit.

The queue at the check-in desk was not too long. Most of the passengers had checked in online and were just dropping their bags off. When she reached the desk she heaved her small wheeled suitcase onto the conveyor belt.

'It's not too heavy, is it?' she asked.

'No, it's well within the limit. It's only twelve kilos, and you're allowed twenty-three. You're fine.'

'Oh good,' Connie said. 'I've got... here's my passport and... I've got a ticket voucher here...' She was furiously searching through a pocket of the carry-on bag.

'That's all right. Your passport is all I need. Here's your boarding pass. The gate number hasn't been announced yet. Check the departure boards for information.'

Freed from her heavy bag, Connie picked up the smaller one by the shoulder strap and started off for Security. She was unsure whether to carry the boarding pass in her hand or stow it somewhere, so she walked along trying to unzip an outer compartment of her travel bag, finding it was too small for her wallet, then groping for the compartment on the other side, then finally, as she neared the security area, giving up and continuing to carry the document wallet in one hand.

You had to put any liquids in a clear plastic bag before even joining the queue for the security gate and the x-ray machine. Connie stopped to read the sign telling you what wasn't allowed. She thought for a moment. Her shampoo, hand lotion, cleanser – all those things were in the suitcase she had checked in.

'Hello. Do you have any liquids? If so, please put them in one of the bags provided.' The attendant must say this a thousand times a day.

'No, I packed them all.'

'Do you have any of these prohibited items? Explosives, sharp items, nail files, knives, scissors, corrosive material, weapons, firearms...'

'Oh no, explosives, firearms! No, none of those. I packed my nail file. Oh! Wait! I do have a pair of scissors! Oh dear.'

'I'm afraid we'll have to confiscate them. You can put them in that bin.'

The bin was half full of all sorts of knives and blades that people had thoughtlessly put in their carry-on bags or pockets instead of their checked luggage. If they didn't forfeit it here it would be found and confiscated at the x-ray machine.

'How silly of me!' Connie said. 'Now I'll have to buy a new pair! Well, it serves me right for being so careless!'

The Heathrow security woman was sympathetic. 'You can always get another pair of scissors. Some people carry expensive things – antique daggers, things like that. They just don't think ahead! We have to confiscate all that kind of thing, no exceptions. Thanks for being so understanding. That bin over there. That's right.'

'Goodness, what happens to them all? Do you return them to their owners later?'

'I believe they go out to auction eventually. You'd think people would learn, but we take in new items all the time.'

'Auction,' Connie repeated. 'So they'll have a new owner.' She shrugged. 'Well, good-bye, scissors.'

Connie went on and joined the queue for Security. She read all the bewildering instructions: remove your coat, put laptops in a separate tray, take metal items out of your pockets... Sometimes they wanted you to take your shoes off and go through the metal-detector doorway in your stocking feet, but that wasn't necessary this time. Connie passed through the doorway without being frisked. They didn't seem very interested in her, and she collected her bag and her jacket.

At last she left the Security zone and was plunged straight into the Duty-Free, which seemed to go on forever, with shelves of all kinds of alcohol, perfume, and cigarettes, and if they couldn't tempt you with any of that there were chocolate bars, tee shirts, key rings, and stuffed toys. Finally she emerged into a general waiting area where you waited until your gate number was shown on the many screens that were fixed high up where they could be seen from a distance.

Connie found a vacant seat and sat down, placing her carry-on bag at her feet and her coat on her lap. Now she could catch her breath after all this hurrying. It was relaxing in spite of the rush and buzz around her – people pulling their suitcases along smartly to a departure gate, people killing time until their gate number was displayed, people drinking coffee and spring water and keeping their children entertained. She took a paperback book out of the bag.

It was a murder mystery, just the thing to relax with after the hurly-burly of getting to the airport on time – getting to the airport on the way home and getting away from Louis. What a weekend! So different from what she had hoped, but he was his same old abusive self. She had been going to surprise him! He would be glad to see her, or so she thought. They would have a lovely weekend together. They would have a romantic dinner on the Saturday. They would be affectionate with each other. They would make love tenderly. They would make up for some of the things that had happened in the past. It would be a new beginning for them. She had even thought of moving to London, getting a job, just to be near Louis! What had she been thinking! Why had she thought he would ever change?

Louis. She hadn't realized how much she actually hated him. She would scarcely have guessed it until this morning when he came at her, hard fists flying, as though he were fighting some other man in a pub brawl! She had suddenly thought – and both thoughts came at the same time: 'Who does he think he is?' and

'I don't have to put up with this!' She was suddenly amazed that she had ever put up with his behaviour, and for so long. And to think, a moment before she had been sewing on a button for him!

But now that was all over, and she opened the book to the page she had reached on the trip to London. The story was rather predictable in its way. It was typical: they found the body in chapter two and now in chapter five they were still looking for the murder weapon.

Maybe they would find it, and maybe they wouldn't.

Maybe it got taken away somewhere. Maybe it was well hidden.

Maybe it ended up in an auction.

## Midday Bus
David Mathews

A handshake, and that was it.

In those days you did not kiss on both cheeks, mua, mua. That was for French people. On the telly, Russians in fur hats hugged, but they were politicians who clapped their own speeches, so goodness knows what ordinary folk did in Minsk or Murmansk. (They were 'Soviets' then, the 'Reds.') Who was it rubbed noses? Indians and Japanese bowed. Did these gestures serve as farewells as well as greetings?

No matter. A handshake. He watched her climb the three ridged, metal steps, walk to the middle of the bus and choose a seat from where she could watch the sea for the first twenty minutes of the ride, right hand side, away from him. He could see her head, nothing more. Cream, with a blue stripe, the bus; more a coach given the high seats, but called bus by the locals.

He nodded to the driver who raised the first finger of his left hand from the wheel by way of answer. The door hissed, moved, stuck for a second, and closed. The gears clunked, the note of the engine deepened and the bus left the kerb to speed down the hill that took you to the pier. Did Laura turn her head to look at him? Maybe. Probably not.

They had been lucky with the day, George and Laura. The height of these cliffs exposed you to the full force of wind and rain when the weather inclined that way. The bus shelter offered protection from the worst of it, but you had to put up with graffiti that, in the main, only an anthropologist would relish, learning that size mattered to some people, mattered a good deal, the dimensions of tits and dicks. Quantity too; you would have guessed that 'MG' still lived with mum and dad, judging by the number of conquests he or she claimed to have made on or about the wooden bench.

Exceptionally, 'Terry' displayed both wit and grammatical competence. He applied his mighty pen to Harold Wilson's cabinet exclusively and with venom, but he knew that government was a singular noun, and that the collective term for both wankers and tossers was 'bunch'.

As a rule, the midday bus was taken by those with no pressure on their time. When you intended to do something with the day other than travel, you gulped your coffee and caught the eight o'clock. The evening bus in winter had a lonesome quality, taking away the lost and the exhausted. In summer, though, you rode off towards the sunset, fair play, some promise there. But Laura's bus, the 1205, adopted a relaxed air, travelling the bulk of its journey while most people were at lunch, rendering it safe from ambush by Devonian bandits. Laura took an egg and cress sandwich for the journey.

George and Laura had said their goodbyes as they walked the mile to the bus stop. Each knew the conversation would be the last between them. She might send him a postcard, to say that she had arrived somewhere, but no letter, nor would she ring. And him? He could not imagine that he would have anything to tell her, not from his own life, not from the goings-on of the town and its hinterland. She had seen it. She had enjoyed it as she found it, but had not become affiliated.

'I wonder how it will feel,' she said, after they had talked about the warmth of the sun and the fading blossom on the hedgerows, and how different the day was from a hard winter.

He guessed she meant leaving.

'For me or you?' he said.

'Both, really.'

For him it would be 'satisfactory', he told her. No elation, no heartbreak, but a feeling of rightness, timeliness, inevitability. He had once needed to re-home a dog he was fond of. It needed many times more exercise than he could give it. He started to draw the analogy, but gave up when the absurdity made them both laugh. A border collie? She guessed right.

'For you, though, what can I say? Leaving? Not like leaving, you know, your childhood home, because home remains home. For a time, maybe years, your room waits for you to pop in and see your teddy bear, sitting on the wrong chair, of course, because there were guests who did not know he liked to look out of the window. Certainly not like leaving a relationship – we've each done that – so none of the anger or guilt ...'

'George, come on, not what it isn't ...'

'I've no basis for saying.' He gave the slow shrug that she had grown to know revealed that he should be pressed to make his point.

'Then what do you hope it might be like, because I suppose you do hope the best for me, don't you? Or what do you imagine? You're always on at me to imagine, to play with an idea?'

He stopped by a gate into a field. Cows at the far end looked up, but did not find the humans interesting. George had a habit of tugging his left ear when he was thinking hard. They were not pressed for time, so she did not rush him as he tugged.

'It could be an outing, I suppose,' he said, 'an excursion, but one that that never ends. Candyfloss, chips, rock salmon, ice-cream, sunburn, being sick, being pickpocketed, not being able to open the deckchair, snogging behind the bogs, pint of winkles, bottle of brown ale, sand in your toes, sand in your knickers. Whatever those things are in real life, that's your outing now.'

'But there's the bus home at the end of the day, when you're hot and dirty and all you want is to wake up in bed asleep.'

'You miss it, the bus. But there is a train.'

'To home?'

'Somewhere else.'

'Better or worse?'

'Doesn't matter. What matters is you choose where to get off. You choose.'

Much of Laura's time with George they had been solitary. He had pottered about house and garden and retreated to his den to write his memoirs, never to be published, sometimes skipping meals for a whole day.

She had explored the coast thirty miles each way, in all weathers, getting her old life out of her system. 'Into perspective' is how she put it, the city, work, lovers, lectureships, research.

But several times a week they cooked and ate together, played scrabble fiercely, did crosswords, ranted at politicians on the news. These were their intimacies, these and minor incidents, opportunities for unforced closeness that created no expectation one of the other.

They had walked through a meadow where sheep grazed, and he found a tick on his calf. He taught her how to remove it with tweezers, making sure not to kill the tiny beast first. She let go too soon, and the tick was on her leg in an instant. They called it Denise after a neighbour who could never take the hint to go home.

George had twisted a knee, and Laura had played nurse until the Monday when the doctor called.

Laura learned, too late for the funeral, of the death of an aunt she loved. She wept in George's arms for an evening.

More than anything, they were close when they pored over books on wildlife, insects especially, with their intense cycles of life, bizarre, unthought-of as you swat them away or squash them. Dragonflies and damsel flies appealed to Laura, the few moments of brilliance through which most people know them seeming paltry compared to the patient larval wait to emerge. She, Laura decided, would not leave until the dragonflies appeared.

George had not intended any of this, this nurturing. He had advertised a room to let with the run of the house. Someone working in the town, he had assumed, happy to be quiet in the house in the evenings and on weekends if they had nowhere else to go. Town, with its seaside businesses and industrial estate, was a car or bike ride away. A person around the house would keep him sharp, give him responsibility, might be fun, but would not stay for ever, would not become important.

No-one phoned, and even Laura did not get round to knocking. She stood beyond the gate, rucksack, woolly hat, hair blowing in an October gale. She had balked at the size of the place and how run-down it seemed, but George, turning his compost, paused, leant on his fork and smiled at her.

'I don't suppose,' she said, disarmed, 'the room?'

George looked at her get-up, and assumed she wanted it for a couple of nights, but no, she was making a change, she said, a month certainly. Did he mind if she left it open beyond that?

*

Thirty years later Laura spoke publicly about George for the first time, on a chat show sofa next to a footballer and a celebrity lawyer. The three had been asked about a person who had influenced them, not formally, not a coach or a teacher, just someone.

She found that she could not describe him. Without a photograph to remind her, his features had blurred. Spectacles, she remembered, and a white moustache – or was it a beard? His demeanour, though, was clear, his calmness, earnestness and humour.

'Invisible man,' said the host, getting the laugh he sought.

'No.' She was sharp in her response.

The host challenged her. 'How should we picture him then, Laura?'

'Telling me a story. Not fiction, but some bit of the world that I knew nothing of. He could be like a little boy – OK a girl could do this, but we think of boys doing it – taking out a matchbox and showing you a spider or a beetle. Weird creatures. Don't know why, but the one I remember is the mud dauber wasp that seals its eggs each in a little cell with live jumping spiders, sedated, so they would be fresh food for the larva.'

'Gross,' said the host, and the audience, on cue, pretended to retch.

'No stranger than what we do, eating cows and sheep and chickens that we take our children to admire.'

The footballer was asked to talk about what he ate before a match, and the delicate problem of timing bowel movements to avoid the crucial couple of hours of a game.

As the audience groaned again, the host ambushed Laura.

'Did he fall in love with you, Laura, this George? He wouldn't be the first. When you left, would he have missed you, cried, drunk too much?'

'What, George? What an idea. No, not George.'

## Walderman's
Becky Ros

It feels strange remembering this, as I'm getting ready to leave Walderman's, but I didn't actually want to come here. How close I came to missing out on the happiest three years of my life. If I had known the campus was in the middle of the Alaskan wilderness when I was asked to apply, I would have dismissed it straight away. I would have proceeded with my initial plan and continued to apply for universities in London with a view to becoming an English teacher at my old school. But that's the great mystery of Walderman's, not only do they not tell you exactly what you will be studying, they don't tell you where in the world it is. After all, they don't want just anyone showing up on campus – only a select few gain access to their hallowed grounds. They make it clear when they suggest you apply that they are very selective, only picking the crème de la crème, and that the education you will receive will be without comparison.

I was approached by, as I discovered later, their only British faculty member. I was at an open day for the University of Roehampton, I'm not sure how he found me, but he told me I was gifted enough to sit their entrance exam and gave me the time, date and his English accent mistakenly lead me to assume the school was in the United Kingdom, and therefore that, if accepted, I'd still be able to see my family at the weekends.

At seventeen I was quite a homebody, and the wrench of having to leave home to go to Higher Education in the first place was out of my comfort zone. A university not even in the same continent as my parents was unimaginable. If I could have stayed in my local town forever I would have been happy, but my parents wanted what was best for me. A university in

London, only a two-hour commute, would be acceptable for all parties. I'd leave home, albeit temporarily, but at least I'd get the experience and sense of independence people my age were meant to crave.

The Walderman's entrance exam itself was held on a Tuesday in late June, in a nondescript office building close to King's Cross station, again wrongly convincing me of the British pedigree of the institution. I did not think to question why the exam was not taking place at the actual university. I was naïve, I wasn't concerned that I couldn't find any reference to Walderman's on the internet or that none of my teachers really knew what it taught, although a few had heard of it. I don't remember much about that morning, I now know it's because the exam was enchanted.

There were five of us at the start and only me at the end, the others having not passed, and gone without me noticing.

I'd always loved magic when I was a child, I used to look forward to the Paul Daniels Magic Show every Saturday night. I wanted to be a magician's assistant when I grew up, because I loved Debbie McGee's outfits. When I was eight, I begged my parents to buy me a magic set for Christmas. I put on endless shows for the family. I was surprisingly good for my age, for any age really, but this was due in large part to the fact that I was doing real magic although I didn't realise it. When I made coins disappear, I wasn't palming them, they really did briefly disappear until I plucked them back from the ether, from behind someone's ear, or sometimes from their nose. I was a kid, I hadn't bothered reading the instructions, so I genuinely thought I was doing what everyone else was doing. If I thought about it hard enough it happened – making pencils float, or cards change suit, it all came naturally to me. After about eighteen months, I think my parents realised there was something uncanny about my magical talents, as they stopped me performing in front of guests or at school. As I got older, magic wasn't cool anymore, so I stopped performing, and almost forgot about my talent. My memories took on the same quality as a half-remembered dream. I wasn't sure if what I had done was real or a story I'd been told, but I knew something wasn't 'normal'.

I tried to supress this special part of me, but someone or something out there knew about it and that's how the staff at Walderman's found me. I assume they must have some kind of radar that senses children not born into practising families, but during my time here I never really felt the need to ask, and now I am leaving it seems unnecessary to find out.

They don't call it magic at Walderman's, the correct term is Thaumaturgy. Students do not concern themselves trying to learn parlour tricks, or sleight-of-hand, to impress people at parties, or make their life a little easier, this is bigger picture magic. Thaumaturgy literally translates as a wonder or miracle working, and that is what I spent three years of my life working towards. It was a lot to take in for someone who was planning a career in education. I wasn't given a lot of time to consider if miracle working was what I wanted to do. After I passed the exam they needed a decision within the hour, or the offer would be revoked.

Once I said yes, there was no going back. It was then that I found out the school was in the middle of Alaska and that their term started in August. I no longer had the summer to mentally and physically prepare for leaving home. Instead of the two car loads of belongings I had planned to take to London, I was now only able to take a suitcase with me. I had to figure out quickly what was really important to me. I had been so reluctant to grow up, and now I had no choice but to grow up fast.

My parents were delighted. I guess they were relieved to find out my special talents were not that special after all. I think they, unlike me, were more than happy to cut the apron strings. I heard them planning to turn my bedroom into a study – empty nesting was not a concern.

And so, with barely a tear shed, they waved me off at Heathrow airport bound for Anchorage and the rest of my life. I got the feeling that they never expected to hear from me again and strangely I felt the same. That part, the mundane part of my life, was over as soon as I had accepted a place at Walderman's. For better or worse, I said goodbye to the homebody me at the airport, and reluctantly embraced the part of me I didn't know existed, the part that wanted an adventure.

I wasn't wrong to feel this way; for the first time, I finally felt like myself. Maybe the reason I'd clung to my home town for so long, was that I was afraid of leaving home, as I knew deep down I might not belong anywhere else. At a university in London there was a danger no one would like or accept someone like me, but without a doubt, I belonged at Walderman's.

Each intake of new students had an equal balance of students from magical and non-magical families from all over the world. Unlike some of my fellow non-magical students I didn't find it hard to accept that magic was real, it made sense and explained why I could always find things other people thought they had lost forever, or mend things that seemed irrevocably broken. Apparently from every first-year class at least two people dropped out as they weren't willing to leave the mundane world behind. They refused to accept the enhanced reality magic brought into their lives, it was too hard for them to adjust. Their minds were cleansed by the university doctors and they were sent home none the wiser, it was never a great loss to the school. From my second year onwards, when the new crop of first years arrived we took bets on which ones would give up on magic and depart before the end of the first month, my choice was always correct. I could always spot the student who'd accidentally found themselves in this crazy place and were crying out for their nice normal mundane lives.

For all my anxiety about leaving home, I ended up staying throughout the semester and only going home at the last possible moment for Christmas. Learning magic was incredibly taxing and at the start, the minutiae involved in casting even the simplest spell was mind-numbing, but the exhilaration of the success was like nothing I had felt before, and I kept chasing that feeling, consuming the curriculum until I was forcibly stopped. I wasn't the only one – we were closely monitored in those first few months as learning magic could be addictive. The result was a small number of burnouts, and worse, deaths; but once you literally survived the first year, the rest was plain sailing.

To say I changed would be an obvious understatement, in my three years I saw things most people will never witness in their life. As career prospects for Thaumaturgy go, it is perhaps no surprise that there are a number of highly sought-after job opportunities for freshly minted wizards. A number of my fellow alumni are set to join the intelligence services or high-level military positions. Despite my initial misgivings about the location being so far away from my beloved home counties, I fell so in love with the campus that I considered a teaching position. Again, I almost couldn't bear to leave somewhere I felt comfortable. But I know that sometimes you have to say goodbye to one part of your life to enable the next part of your life to begin. I'm ready to embark on my next big adventure. To pay the bills I am going into the world of finance, many companies and banks in the private sector like to have a wizard or two tucked away on their board in an advisory capacity. In my free time I will continue my studies in the field, tracking down magical beings in their natural habitat and learning their secrets. Although I am leaving my college and friends behind, I know they will always be there if I need them in the future, just as my parents and home town will always be there too.

### Three Sisters on the Edge
Joan Taylor-Rowan

'Just behave like we're on a regular day out at the seaside,' Diana said, marching down the beach with a painted kitchen stool. Her sisters were both standing near the car with their own favourite chairs from their mother's house. A picnic by the sea in honour of their mother – Diana's idea of course. Lizzie and Rosemary watched her make her way through the clumps of sea kale, and then set out after her. Wispy clouds streaked the blue sky and the water scraped at the shingle with the minimum of effort.

'Remind me, why did we agree to this?' Lizzie said, stopping for a moment to push strands of mousy hair behind her ears.

'Because we were exhausted, and Diana's bossy,' Rosemary answered.

'I thought she'd seemed a bit preoccupied these last couple of days.'

'Maybe she's on the change,' Rosemary said smiling, so that her dark eyes were almost lost in her fat pink cheeks.

'Maybe she'll change into the shy, retiring, type,' Lizzie said. 'No malingering you two. The tide's on the turn so hurry up,' Diana called out.

Lizzie scrunched up her face, 'I spoke too soon. Mussolini's back.' They trudged down the beach with their chairs as ordered.

'We look like we're having a jumble sale!' Rosemary said. 'Why didn't we just bring deckchairs like normal people?'

Diana sighed. 'We don't have to be like everyone else, do we?' She raised her arms above her head pressing her palms together and then breathed out noisily. Lizzie still envied that halo of red hair, that pre-Raphaelite face, even though she wanted to punch it. How come Diana got the good genes?

'I still don't see what was wrong with scattering the ashes in the crematorium garden,' Rosemary said, placing her chair next to Lizzie's.

Diana turned from her sun salutation. 'The crematorium garden! It's like a Lidl for the dead.'

'I like Lidl actually. They do very nice bread,' Rosemary said.

'Let's not go over that again. We all agreed we'd scatter the ashes at sea. There were people in tracksuits at those other funerals. Mum wouldn't want to spend eternity there.' Lizzie leaned back in her chair, inhaling the dusty smell. It was an old canvas one that their mother used to take into the garden to read *Oliver Twist* – back when she could still read. The book was a dog-eared essay prize, the thin paper ruffled at the edges. There were torn recipes and knitting patterns marking her place. 'I wonder why Mum loved that book so much,' Lizzie said.

'She was always hoping she was well-connected and that some long-lost relative would come out of the woodwork to tell her she was loaded. But all she got was Dad.'

Lizzie grimaced. 'Ooh I don't like the idea of somebody coming out of the woodwork.'

'Like a cockroach,' Rosemary said, waving her hands like feelers. 'Although Dad was more rat than cockroach.'

Diana wobbled on one leg. 'No one is ever quite what they seem.'

Lizzie was comforted to see that despite all that yoga their younger sister was getting fat round the middle. *Blousey* mother would have said – well if she'd been talking about Rosemary or Lizzie that is. She would have called Diana *voluptuous*.

'He left Mum to raise three toddlers alone. Nothing to misunderstand there Diana, and having a flat in Cannes doesn't suddenly exonerate him, not in my book at least.'

Diana dropped her arms. 'What's that supposed to mean?'

'Just saying, he isn't the only one that buggers off when things get difficult.'

'Stop it right there you two. No squabbling. We're here to bury the dead. Come on Rosie. Help me get the table out of the car.'

Rosemary ground her jaw.

Diana dropped her head and clasped her ankles. 'Well we've got a good day for it anyway,' she called out through her legs.

'Yes, it said that on my *Thought for the Day* calendar,' Lizzie shouted back. 'Today is a perfect day to dispose of your mum's ashes.'

'You are always so snarky about everything, but I know it's just fear. Death is as real as it gets and it will happen to all of us, Lizzie.'

'By drowning if she's not careful,' Lizzie whispered as they hauled the picnic table and the hamper out of the Volvo. Rosemary giggled.


It had been six months since their mother's death. Dying wasn't like in the movies, Lizzie thought. You didn't get the smells in the movies, or the textures; carpet sticky with trodden-in food, surfaces fluffy with dust, the stench of urine. You didn't get to see someone you loved turn into a distorted doppelganger of themselves. It made you want to blow up government departments. Well that was how Lizzie felt. No doubt when it was Diana's turn she would be wafted off to paradise on a lotus leaf, her soul the colour of their mum's lilac bathroom. Diana had been teaching yoga in Italy while Lizzie and Rosemary had been cleaning their mother's bottom, and mopping up sick. 'I just can't do illness,' Diana had said, on one of her brief returns home. 'Blood, urine, vomit, eughh'. She'd left a thank-you card with a picture of the Buddha and £300.

Rosemary seethed when she saw it even though it was typical Diana, breezing through life, with the self-centredness and confidence of the most-loved. Rosemary on the other hand waded through life like a labrador in a swamp – gathering insults and slights like burrs, leaving her loveable but prickly.

'Who's got the ashes anyway?' Rosemary asked, her plump arms gripping the table legs as she paused for breath. 'Did you bring them, Liz?'

'No, Diana has them. They're in that bag over there next to her coat. The one that says CHOOSE LIFE.'

Rosemary snorted and dropped her end of the table.


The day before, they'd gathered in the old house to plan the picnic. Diana said they should bury the ashes at low tide so they would be washed away as it came in.

'I'm not sure we're allowed to bury them, actually,' Rosemary had said. 'I thought we could cut a hole in some carrier bags and walk along the beach, you know, letting it dribble out.' She stuck one leg out and shook it and then did the same with the other as she took a chocolate from the tin and walked back to her armchair. Diana choked on her tea, spilling it down her dress.

'You mean have bags down our trousers like in *The Great Escape*?' Lizzie had said. 'If I'd known I wouldn't have worn my skinny jeans. I'll never get a bag of ashes down these.'

They'd all collapsed with laughter. Diana had decided it for them. 'The Universe will tell us when we get there.'


'Watch out,' Rosemary said, 'dogs at three o'clock.'

Lizzie grabbed the bag with the ashes in it. 'Do ashes smell? I mean they are dogs – this is bone. This could be a disaster!'

Diana leaned back in her chair unperturbed as a dog licked her feet. 'The ashes are in a canister, didn't you look? I think it's like powder.'

'Powder, really? I imagined it like cat litter,' Lizzie said. 'Maybe with bits of vertebrae.'

'Oh please Lizzie!' Rosemary said.

Although the dogs were now safely in the distance, Rosemary was still anxious. 'Can we just get this done, before anyone else comes along? I don't want us all arrested for illegal disposal of human remains.'

'Don't worry,' Diana said. 'It'll be fine. Now have we got the feast for afterwards?'

Lizzie held up the picnic basket and a bottle of Cava.

'So this is it…' Rosemary said. 'Final goodbyes and all that.'

'Well her soul's been gone a while now, if you believe in that stuff. This is like her coat that she left behind. It's not really her, is it?'

'Well put, Sis. We're just throwing her coat into the sea for her onward journey,' Diana said.

Rosemary was cradling the bag in her lap, the handles wrapped tightly around her fingers.

Lizzie stroked her arm. 'It's alright, Rosie, we're all at sea.'

Rosemary's chin quivered. 'Is that why my eyes are swimming?'

Lizzie chuckled and squeezed her hand. She took the food out of the hamper and arranged the containers on the table. A seagull swooped and squawked above them and they all ducked.

'That would just about do me in, if a seagull flew off with her,' Rosemary sniffed.

'She'd probably squeal with excitement, like she did when they first lifted her in the hoist.'

Rosemary laughed and dabbed her eyes. 'Yeah we all thought she'd be terrified, but that was the one thing she looked forward to in the House of Doom.'

'We did our best, Rosie. Twenty-four-hour care they said for those last months. We couldn't have done that, we'd have been madder than her.'

'I know, I know,' Rosemary said, caressing the bag.

'Let's make a toast and say what we need to say,' Diana said, her voice a little choked.

'Oh God, here we go.'

'Look Lizzie, you don't have to say anything if you don't want to, but most parting ceremonies involve music and prayers for the deceased to help them transit from this world to the next.' Diana leaned over and rummaged among the bags and clothes she'd dumped on the beach. She pulled out a case.

'Holy moley,' Lizzie said. 'That is either your old violin or a machine gun, and I really hope it's a machine gun.'

'Oh what a comedian you are, and yes it is my violin.' Diana stood up tucking the instrument under her chin. She shifted her stance, wriggled her shoulders.

'But you can't even play the violin! You never even bothered to learn it. Mum spent all that money on your violin and then there was none left for my riding lessons,' Rosemary said.

'That was a long time ago. We were just children.'

'Some of us still are,' Lizzie said. 'You are not planning to play that now are you? I mean, seriously. This is a public place. There might be people with mental health problems.'

'There will be if she starts playing,' Rosemary said.

'I know the basics. Mum always said I had a delicate touch.' She began to pass the bow across the strings.

Lizzie remembered Rosemary changing her mother's dressings. 'Oh, you're such a clumsy oaf, Rosemary. Where's my Diana?' Lizzie could see now that fleeting, stricken look on Rosemary's face before the practical Rosemary returned. 'Well it's me or nothing, Mum, and I'm doing my best.' 'At least she still knows who I am,' she'd said later.

Rosemary winced as the violin screeched. She pressed her fingers to her forehead. 'Please Diana, stop that appalling noise.'

Diana closed her eyes, her large breasts jiggling as she sawed away at the strings. In the distance a dog howled, then another. Lizzie thought about forks scraping saucepans, adorable kittens being stepped on.

She looked across at her sister, hoping for their normal conspiratorial smirk at all things Diana, but Rosemary was flushed and her hands were balled into fists. She stood up, nearly tipping the table over as she thumped it.

'Stop that, just stop that.' She grabbed the bow from Diana.

'I knew you'd do this, hijack the event. You always hijack everything. This isn't about you, Diana, it's about Mum. It's about us – all three of us. You may have been her favourite but where were *you* when we were cleaning up the mess and dealing with her heebie jeebies in the middle of the night – where were you then?'

Diana bit her lower lip. She clutched the violin to her chest. 'That's not fair.'

'Fair, we're talking about fair now, are we?' Rosemary was leaning across the table which was sinking into the shingle, like a doomed ship. Lizzie put her hand out to Rosemary, but she would not be stopped.

'Every bloody thing I wanted we couldn't have because we had no money, but somehow you still managed to get what you wanted, violin, roller skates, drama lessons – like you needed any help there!' She paused for breath.

Lizzie was looking at the table, at the small canister of gunpowder that was fuelling this explosion. Their mother would have hated to hear them shouting in public, it was so common, but before she could interject, Rosemary burst out again.

'Then not only do you suddenly become scarce when the dementia sets in – but when she went into the hospital, when we needed you there with us, you send a postcard from fucking France, saying you were with Dad. How did you even find him? He hadn't given a shit for the last forty years, but you decide to get lovey-dovey with him. What is wrong with you?'

Diana sank into her chair, a galleon beached by the storm that had just blown in. 'You don't understand,' she murmured.

'No of course I don't. I'm just dull, boring, dutiful Rosemary who doesn't understand anything.' She folded her arms across her chest as if to hold herself back.

Diana rubbed her eyes. She was looking older, Lizzie thought, they all were. They were all motherless old children now.

'There is something I have to tell you.'

Rosemary rolled her eyes, looked to Lizzie for support. 'Oh here we go.'

Diana held up her hands. 'Let me finish. It's Dad, he… he isn't my father.'

'What! Oh please!' Rosemary shook her head. 'When did this all come out then, was it in one of your rebirthing sessions or was it that charlatan you visited in Glastonbury?'

'It was Gloucester and she was a psychotherapist, actually, but she's got nothing to do with it. And for the record Rosie, I didn't look for him, he found me. It was just when Mum went into the hospital. It was so weird. I was about to lose my mother and then out of the blue my invisible dad gets in touch. I thought it was the Universe trying to balance things out. I shouldn't have sent you the postcard about the flat in Cannes but when I met him, he wasn't this loser we'd all been led to believe. He was just this regular old man, with a nice apartment by the sea. I thought maybe he wanted to make contact with us all again.'

Diana fiddled with the large silver ring on her index finger. 'But it was a couple of days later when I found out why he'd really got in touch.'

'I'm confused,' Rosie said. 'So who is your dad then, and how long has our dad known he wasn't your dad?'

'He had a mate, Sam. He died a few months before Mum, and Dad found letters from her. There was a holiday, sailing, all three of them were there, and you two apparently. Mum always loved the sea.' She brushed at her cheek with the back of her hand.

'All the nice girls love a sailor,' Lizzie said to the horizon. She was watching some youngsters playing on a lilo, splashing and laughing like they'd done at that age, before the world got its hooks in and messed them up. Her curlered, crimpled mum, having an affair. It seemed so unlikely. She tried to recall that trip, but she'd been too young. There were photos, but no third man that she remembered. Rosemary would have been three, did she remember him? Who looked after them both when the adults were all out sailing – or did Dad sit on the beach with them while Mum was off with Sam in some cove? A scene from an old film of surf crashing on writhing bodies popped into her head. She tried to shake it away.

'So that's why Dad left, because she had an affair… and got pregnant with you?' Rosemary said.

Diana laughed, wryly. 'Alas, no. He knew nothing about it. He assumed I was his. He was just a player – these are his words not mine – not cut out for fatherhood.'

'Hmm, took him three times to realise that, did it – bit slow on the uptake,' Lizzie said.

'Those final few days when we were all with her in the hospice,' Diana said. 'That was one of the worst times in my life. Dad had dropped this big bombshell and I couldn't even ask her about it. I was furious with her for not telling me, and I couldn't tell you both, not then. I know what you thought of me dashing off again straight after the funeral, but I was in a bit of a mess. And since then I just couldn't seem to find the right moment. I wanted to tell you yesterday but we were having fun and I didn't want to spoil it.'

Lizzie was in turmoil. A wave of exhilaration that Diana wasn't one of them had been followed almost instantly by another larger wave of pity. Diana was on her own, outside the gang. She'd have felt small and lost and alone, abandoned by two fathers.

'Bugger it. Now I'm supposed to feel sorry for you,' Rosemary said. 'But… Christ! Mum, an affair, I can't believe it. And Dad didn't even know? How did he take that?'

Diana shrugged. 'In a way it made it easier for him. Old men get maudlin, you know, full of regret. Finding out she'd cheated on him made him feel better about being a useless father. He felt like he deserved it.'

'He did deserve it,' Rosemary said. 'Not a letter or card after the first two years. I suppose he'll want to be friends now, the shit.'

Lizzie toyed with the violin bow. Her mother would have loved to hear gossip like this, if it hadn't been about her. She missed those calls with her mother – the dry exchanges, the acid tongue. She'd always thought they had a special bond, but her mother hadn't been able to talk about this.

Lizzie looked up, and Diana's shoulders were shaking. She reached across the table and took her hand.

'Don't cry. Don't, it's ok,' she said.

'It's not ok.' Diana sniffed. 'It means you two aren't my sisters.'

'We're half-sisters,' Lizzie said, 'and two half-sisters make a whole sister. But we still want a present each on our birthdays.'

Diana laughed and wiped her nose on the back of her hand.

'I'm sorry about the violin.'

'Not half as sorry as we are. God, I just can't believe it though. I think I need a drink.'

Lizzie opened the wine with a shaky hand. The cork flew across the table and hit the water. She poured them each a glass.

They all stared at the bag on the table. Lizzie had been a toddler when Dad left. She thought she could remember shouting, plates thrown, but it was hard to know what was real and what was not. Dad had become a fiction, a mean little character embroidered by her mother on their Home Sweet Home sampler.

'Ok, let's get this over with,' Rosemary said.

She leaned down into her handbag. 'I brought a trowel.'

They walked together down to the sea's edge. The wind ruffled the surface but there were no waves. Rosemary scanned the horizon. 'The coast is clear,' she said. She leaned over and tried to dig a hole. It filled with water. 'Hmmm. Well that's not going to work, is it?'

Lizzie fumbled in her pocket. 'I know you'll think I'm really, like over-prepared, but I made this bag – it's soluble fabric, so we can put the ashes in it and just fling it into the water and it will dissolve.'

Rosemary tilted her head, impressed. 'And I thought you'd mock my trowel.'

Lizzie held the bag open, Rosemary put in a couple of stones and Diana opened the canister and poured in the ashes, fine dust, not like cat litter at all.

Lizzie knotted the top with some string. 'It'll all melt away,' Lizzie said. 'No turtles will be harmed in the disposing of these ashes.'

Diana looked up the beach where a family were arriving with striped bags and windbreaks and a small yapping dog. 'We can't just throw it. People might think we are chucking in rubbish.'

Rosemary cleared her throat. 'Right. Lizzie roll up your trouser legs, Diana hitch up your skirt – we're going in.'

They held each other's hands, Lizzie clutching the bag as they stepped into the water.

'Bloody hell – it's freezing!' Rosemary wailed, stamping her feet. 'I'll get rheumatism!'

'Do you remember that time,' Lizzie said between gasps, 'when Mum could still hobble and I took her in for a paddle? She shrieked like a banshee when the waves hit her and then burst out laughing. Then that old seadog helped her back up to the car and people cheered. She never stopped talking about it.'

'*The lure of the sea,*' Rosemary said.

'She brought us all the way here on the bus with the cousins in tow. Auntie Izzy covered us in olive oil and left us to play in the sun. I looked like a boiled prawn by the end,' Diana said.

'Couldn't do that now, you'd be done for child abuse,' Rosemary said.

The water, cold, refreshing, life-giving, slapped their legs. Ferries cruised back and forth, and out at sea the container ships glided across the skyline, heading to China, Mexico and Spain. They paused, watching the world carry on without their mother. Then Diana scooped up a handful of water and threw it at Lizzie.

'Don't, Don't! My bag might dissolve and I'll be covered in Mum.'

Rosemary screeched with laughter. She swished her hand through the surface and lobbed Diana back.

'OK. This is it,' Lizzie said. 'This is the moment.' She swung the bag in her left hand. 'Here she goes!' She threw it out to sea and they waved goodbye as the last remains of their mother landed with a splash a few feet away. As the bag began to dissolve small bubbles popped up to the surface.

'She's having the last word even now,' Lizzie said.

They stood hand-in-hand watching the dissolving scraps floating on the waves like a lotus flower, before disappearing at last into the gleaming west.

# Trail
Zoe Brigley

*When a man you love spends years telling you that you're crazy, that is not an easy mythology to escape.*
– Kelly Sundberg

You switch the engine off and glance at the back seat, where she is ordering the jumble of coats, hats and gloves. Snow is blowing across windscreen, white against the black pines – meteorites or stars streaming through space. The windscreen wipers have stopped, so snow begins to coat the glass. You glance back again. She tugs at her sock before reaching under the seat for her boot. She does not look or speak, so you pull your hat down over your ears and shove the door open.

At first you can't feel the cold, muffled by layers of wool: sound heard through water, or rumbling like a radio at low volume. A van is parked a few paces down the road but the snow has drifted in a huge curve against its side, the way the sea sculpts the sand in waves against fortifying walls. You turn towards the wind that rushes up the hillside, fine snow stinging bare cheeks. Over the points of pines are the dark shapes of houses: the church spire is a finger pointing up. The town is circled, blinded by snow. The car door thumps: a glimpse of her coat flitting pale blue between the pines. You lock up the car, checking the door before following.

You're not surprised by her disappearance. You chased her before on that day you argued: a sweltering evening on a bus heading back into the city. She sat silent, stared out into hot rain until you reached the stop, then barged past you into the aisle, leaped out onto the pavement. When you stepped off, her heels were clacking on the concrete as she ran. You saw her trip at the corner, before she disappeared.

No rush to catch her up, you jingled the change in your pocket, sauntered after her savouring the thick air and the patter of rain spotting your shirt. Droplets fell from your nose, dribbled down your cheeks and chin, but your ringing steps were lighter, free of the dead weight that she'd hung on you all day. Besides, you knew where she'd be, curled on the doorstep without a key, her clothes clinging and wet. You dragged her to her feet, felt the flimsy weight of her body thump against the wooden door when you pushed her.

Now in the snow, you enjoy the chase when you glimpse her blue coat through the trees. Your head tingles, like that evening when you struggled on the doorstep in the rain. You kept her tight against your hip, your arm round her waist. The key in your hand blundered towards the lock.

It stops snowing. Fir trees are heavy with white; branches bend under the weight. The footprints you walk in grow deeper. Trees grow closer together. Needles catch on your coat sleeves, the leg of your trousers. The sky is dark now through black knitted branches. The moon is bright against it.

In front of you, a patch of black on the snow: her glove. In snow thigh-deep, you stretch out an arm to reach it. The leather fingers are stiff, the lining silver. But no sign at all of a body in the snow: the hand that caught the crook of your arm, rubbed its palms over your body.

You begin to dig, pulling clothes out of the drift, a magician plucking coloured handkerchiefs. Here a blue coat clumped with snow. Here a damp silk blouse, and here a gauzy bra. You keep digging, and reach her boots as it begins to snow again.

# Poems

## The Flight of the B52s
Elinor Brooks


Deep unease
on the edge of sleep
on the verge of war:
an engine roar
distant, low, persistent
reverberates inside my womb.
Beneath, between, among the sheets
over and over
it wakes me between worlds.

Stumbling from bed to bathroom
I clutch the blind and sway:
in front of the sky
the tree-tops loom
great clots of darkness
clumped together
against a growing grey.
Gravity is drawing me down
and dragging at me.

In the morning, sunshine.
People leave their homes
for work or school
visit neighbours
buy the papers.
Above their heads
unseen by most
presides the moon
perfectly round and pale:

the bloodshed has begun.

## Learning to Tell the Time
Elinor Brooks


When the big hand is at the top
the doors of the ward open.

Mummies come flooding through them
clutching little packages
and disappear from view – except for mine.

She sits by my bed and talks,
but I do not hear her.

Over her shoulder I watch
the hand inch round:
will a miracle prevent its
downward progress
stop my heart
from falling
crashing
into the
number
six?

Too late, she's gone.

**Flying Ants Day**
Elinor Brooks

One humid summer day you'll see
these daughter queens

push through cracks you barely knew were there
wings like rolled spinnakers laid along their backs

and you'll sense beneath the kitchen floor
the frantic massing of a slender sisterhood
drawn singly into light
                                        one behind the other.

They fill the sky with pheromones
            stirring clouds of males
                                        across the town
                        to give them chase.
                                                    They'll
mate with
                        the fittest, fastest, as many as strength will
allow

                                    until they fall

fuelled in-flight with sperm enough
to last a lifetime laying eggs

the wings they chewed from their own backs
discarded in the earth.

### Running
Nancy Charley


No one knew who set them,
       how smooth beds
     became stacked with boulders
          briskening brooks' babbles to brawl.

Some said they were cairns –
       sacred places
sited by a pilgrim on a mission for peace –
     sprinkled salt in penitence.

Others claimed they were devilment,
      impish work,
        clagging
       the course of natural lives.

She wanted to believe in the science of erosion
       but that summer
           they tracked
   from mouth to source

every spot where the current crescendoed
          he slipped her grasp,
      mickle eyed,
    and willing her

              to set him free.

## Bear Mother
Math Jones


Bear now has more bones than she can carry,
   cub still in her arms.
The creak of trees in her legs, in her back.
Claws worn to the pad.
She wants to lie down, become a mountain;
   to let autumnal flesh drop,
   teeth roll away.
To lay her head upon her mother's soft swell.
> *Look, child,*
> *there is honey in the high tree, fish*
> *in the stream, ants beneath*
> *the heavy beam. Run, climb, swim.*
Lips on her ancient gum, tongue on her nose,
   snuffle of a child old enough to know,
   opens up to a last roar, *Go!*
> *Live! As long as you can.*
> *I have no more power.*
NOR DO I, CHILD, I WILL TAKE THE LAST
YOU HAVE;
YOUR CUB WILL KEEP THE BIT YOU GAVE.
And then, she is gone.

**Tonight, I Leave This Town**
Math Jones


Could the light have fallen differently?
*A planet cannot change its orbit even by an inch,*
*nor slow its satellite; the clouds were always*
*going to be just where they were,* but
   if she had not come in, then,
   and pulled the blind, if the bulb
   in the hall had been replaced,
   if he'd arrived just minutes earlier,
   worn a different colour, or even
   turned his head…

*No planet can alter its orbit even by an inch,*
*nor slow its satellite,*
*nor cease to spin.*

   …or blinked an eye…

*The stars had been the same.*

...if the curtain had been closed,
the lamp switched off,
a candle lit,
a fire burning in the grate;
if a car had come along the lane
and turned the corner,
throwing panes across the wall,
or an ambulance had beat its blues across
                              the remnants of a fight;

    perhaps then the light,
*the light*
    might have fallen differently.

    The blink of a new message on the phone
    a new star born in the Milky Way,
    the ring still on her finger,
    the table polished,
    or if there had been less dust?

## Him of the Sea
Math Jones

He was rolling a little in the waves.
I could see that much from the cliff-top.
Bare-chested and green-trousered,
Like the sea was nosing him to shore,
Faithful thing. But hard to shift,
He would fall back, a loyal one himself,
To the blue and grey beneath the white spray.

His muscles seemed all surrendered,
Like the weeds dancing on the current;
I never saw such a bulk of power
Given up. I wondered could he possibly be drowned,
Running to the downward path dug into chalk,
Imagining the scrape the shale and shells
Would make, the water in his lungs.

Slowed by speed upon the pebble reach,
And shorter than the rise, the journey
Hid the sodden man, until a crest and slide,
Avalanche of slipping heels and scuffed hands,
Brought me to the flat sand of low tide,
To a skin made iridescent by the sea,
And swelling and enticing shoulders flung wide.

My call was pitiful like gulls. My grip
Insufficient to surround his wrist. My push
Was made pathetic by the failures of the sea.
My eyes would not accept the shine
Around his thigh and knee, bright scale gleaming.
But pushing palm touch upon his skin,
Soft with salt, giving just a little.

They burn me now, my hands, and as I fell
Below the great wave that came at last,
And bore him all away, I saw his face, the mouth
I'd meant to blow my life into, the gills
Upon his neck - he never needed breath from me at all...
I might have liked though to have kissed the sea
Upon his lips, before he went, to no avail.

## On Leaving London
Gloria Sanders


A pigeon feather floats down
and comes to rest on my shoulder.
Is this London seeing me off
with a winged goodbye?
A tiny part of what makes the Big Smoke
so quaintly, pestilently, smoky.
The colour of a cloud and
the structure of a whole fishbone,
an airborne fish scale
scaling the heights of the soaring grey buildings.
The science teacher talking with pride
about the potassium he put in birdseed,
to make fireflies of Nelson's pals,
comes to mind.

**Physio**
Gloria Sanders


She tells me it's not bone it's tendon
that click click clicks
with every step, curls my toes
when rooms are silent.

Side by side
young and old
treated to questions,
abuse anecdotes, of self-uncare

then two too beautiful Greek women,
Grandmother and Granddaughter, laugh gleamingly.
Their tendons don't click click click
as they alight. Their lightness allowing

the clutternoise of mechanism to drown their bodies'
joint percussion.

Will you holiday? Will we see you abroad?
Stefan wants to clean up loose ends
before talking to hotels.
Stefan has uneven knees
and won't be walking up any mountains
Yet / Again / Soon.
Stefan didn't punch
the physiotherapist.

### Laundry/Camino
Gloria Sanders


If I close my eyes this minute, now,
no pre-planned right eye first then left eye,
no, right now
this wet laundry weight pulling back my shoulders
making me zigzag unsteadily up the road,
could be my snail shell
and this soft light and heat
could be Mediterranean
and that engine vrooming by
could be a tractor checking on vines
and this ache inside
could be a longing for some bread and water or
wine from a tap and this breeze
could be coming over the mountains
and this cardboard carton of concentrate
could be a box of peaches
and the door in which I'm about to turn my key
could be my pilgrim's resting place for the night.
But once I'm hanging out this washing
it could all feel like such a long time ago
and a long time away,
and the dents in my shoulders
will have taken just ten minutes to form,
when what I wish for is a day's worth of dents,
again, and again, and again.

## Terminal

Joy Howard


I've signed up for the house of the dead
and am waiting for my sisters, my sons.
Tell them to meet me – here
where I'm queuing to go in.

Anxious now – no sign of them –
I go on anyway, my shoulders accepting
the sludge-brown weed-green
drape of the dead  – it marks me out.

Led on by the light but resolve on the wane
I ask my guide can I go back
don't think I'm ready and he says yes
but I lose sight of him.

A wanderer now in no-place, I beg
of a stranger  I want to go back,
but the drape clings, if I'm wearing it
will it bind me?

Waxen faced   interrupted
in some sort of intricate working
but kind   he smiles and says not at all
I've been this way twice already.

## Over
Joy Howard

She said 'your eyes look sad
they are like the sea'

and so were hers
a sparkling sunlit sea

as she went on talking
about someone else

## Air Traffic Controller
Joy Howard


prickles of green light
dance a night sky traverse

to the goers-out
and comers-in
I am their little god
their deus locus
to whom they make libations
hands clasped in another's
or interlaced in solitude
as they pray

sky high
or safely landed
their lives assume
an ordinary face

all night
the screens flicker on

## Dorothy Parker Goes on a Day Trip to Criccieth
Joy Howard

I sat and watched the pearly sea
curl onto steely sand

I saw a ruined castle
still guarding sea and land

I heard three ancient women
conversing on the strand

I didn't see a rainbow
there wasn't one to hand

So back to the Metropolis –
get well and truly canned

## Homing
Kate Foley


Hooves? In Amsterdam?
Not the lumbersome-cumbersome
beer-wagon dray-horse thunderings
but light as a very small
clip-clop, dapple-coated
dream, tail a mere whisk
of leaves on the pavement.

But don't turn or you'll see
a herd of jaded tourists,
cases trotting sprightly
on their little wheels
over the up-and-down
Amsterdam flags, careless
knickers and tired shirt cuffs
poking from the zip.

## Airport
Kate Foley


Stately planes.
Nose-cones sniff
a trail
over the ironed
asphalt
under immaculate
clouds.

Little-dog
luggage trucks
truffle,
hold to door,

where travellers swarm and hover
and wait for their stowed identity
to come, familiar as a family pet,
back to their opened hands.

Imagine a far future.
Planes immobile, draped
with strange, dark leaves.
Grasses poke from their nostrils.
Asphalt is now black gravel,
green-stained soil

and one solitary traveller
wonders
what kind of beast they see.

**Green Lanes**
Kate Foley

ancient and mysterious
still funnel under our one-crop fields,
burrow beneath our lamed brick,
our tired concrete
and our minds.

Aerial photographs, crop marks,
prove the buzzard's-eye view.

Remember when you were six –
how in the garden you might have been
a green blade paring sunlight
out of the blue –
and later, how you saw shining boulders
of wooded hills, fretted with cool shadow,
leaning over all your
unresolved futures?

Now, in a season of drought,
when ferrous grasses nose
through the pastures, when hedges
wilt and the bright, consumptive colours
of autumn burn, too early,
in the gutters,
you need to remember
the pilgrim travel of the green lanes,
and risk their only direction.

## ABOUT ARACHNE PRESS

Arachne Press is a micro publisher of (award-winning!) short story and poetry anthologies and collections, novels including a Carnegie Medal nominated young adult novel, and a photographic portrait collection.

We are expanding our range all the time, but the short form is our first love. We keep fiction and poetry live, through readings, festivals (in particular our Solstice Shorts Festival), workshops, exhibitions and all things to do with writing.

Follow us on Twitter:
@ArachnePress
@SolShorts

Like us on Facebook:
ArachnePress
SolsticeShorts2014